Easy
Beauty
Recipes

Making Your Own
Personal-Care Products
in Minutes for Pennies

by Mariah Jager

Easy Beauty Recipes

....

Making Your Own Personal-Care Products in Minutes for Pennies

....

by Mariah Jager

Ottenheimer
PUBLISHERS, INC

Contents

Introduction

Why Choose Homemade?...12
Personal Pampering Made Easy...12
A Word about Safety...14

Chapter 1

The Easy Beauty Pantry....17
Tools of the Trade...17
Super Beauty Staples...19
Picking Produce and Other Ingredients...24
It's Prep Time!...25
Bottling and Storing...25
Weights and Measurements...27

Chapter 2

Beautiful Skin...29
Soothing Baths...30
Simple Soaps...34
Wake-Up Shower Washes and Gels...36
All-Over Moisturizers...40

Chapter 3

The Pampered Face...45
Start-the-Day Splashes...46
Masks...49
Scrubs and Cleansers...54
Wrinkle Relief...61
Oily Skin Repair...64
Dry-Skin Remedies...67
Facial Toners...70
Cold Creams...73
Luscious Lip Balms...75
Eye and Neck Creams...78
Skin Bracers and Aftershaves...81

Chapter 4

Healthy Hair...85
Basic Beauty Shampoos...86
For Oily Hair Only...90
Dry-Hair Revivers...94
Dandruff Treatments...98
Detanglers and Conditioners...101
Buildup Removers...105
Hair Lighteners and Color Enhancers...107
Gray Hair Cover-Up...112

Chapter 5

Nails: Strong and Shapely...113
Cuticle Care...114
Nail Strengtheners...118
Nail Oils and Color Treatments...121
Hand Softeners...125

Chapter 6

A Dazzling Smile...127
Tooth Powders...129
Oral Rinses...133
Mouthwashes...136
Breath Fresheners...138

Chapter 7

Unforgettable Fragrances...141
Toilet Waters...142
Colognes...147
Scented Powders...152
Your Personal Scent Wardrobe...154

Chapter 8

Massage Magic...155
Essential Massage Oils...156
Sore-Muscle Solutions...162
An Introduction to Aromatherapy...164

Chapter 9

For Your Feet...169

Corn and Callus Removers...170
Soothing Footbaths...173
Reviving Foot Rubs...177
Rough-Skin-Softening Lotions...179
· Foot Powders...181

Chapter 10

Easy Beauty Gifts...185

Special Occasions...185
Bottles, Baskets, and Bows...187
Mail-Order Resources...188
Conversion Charts...189, 190

And all the loveliest things there be come simply, so it seems to me.

-Edna St. Vincent Millay

Introduction

What if you had to pay a toll to get ready to face the world each morning? Imagine someone standing outside your bathroom door, hand out, demanding that you pay five dollars to enter. You'd be pretty unhappy, right? Well, that's basically what millions of us do every day without blinking an eye.

If you're like most Americans, you buy shampoos, conditioners, toothpaste, lotions, face and body creams, body soaps, lip balms, and deodorants that add up to hundreds of dollars a year.

The worst part is that in many cases you're not even paying for quality ingredients. Over-the-counter beauty products are chock-full of preservatives, additives, and harsh chemicals, such as isopropyl alcohol, that may not even be good for your skin and hair. Where does all your money go? For marketing and advertising, that's where. Sure, you can try to buy "all-natural" products, but the price tag for them is even higher.

So what's a smart consumer to do? Why not make your own!

You *can* do it. By using natural products found in any grocery store, you can make your very own personal-care products, including shampoos, conditioners, lotions, face powders, lip gloss, toothpaste, colognes—and many more.

WHY CHOOSE HOMEMADE?

The real benefit of homemade personal-care products isn't just the money you save. The real benefit is that these products can actually be better for you. Think about it: If you make your own products, you can tailor them to fit your special cleansing needs, skin type, or favorite fragrance. Plus, because you've made them yourself, the products won't contain any surprise—and possibly harmful—ingredients. Instead of harsh artificial chemicals, you'll be using all-natural ingredients, such as soothing yogurt, fragrant essential oils, and cleansing white vinegar.

What's more, because these simple ingredients are so inexpensive, your personal-care products will cost less than those you buy ready-made in a store. Hard to believe? Let's consider the face creams you buy to smooth your skin and diminish wrinkles. On average, these products cost between five and ten dollars for about five ounces of cream—about a dollar an ounce. Buy the oils and fruit juices to make your own and, for the same price, you can make enough to last throughout the year.

And these products are surprisingly simple to make. Most recipes contain no more than four or five ingredients. The process is similar to cooking a basic meal: a little measuring, a little mixing, maybe some cooking or chilling, and you're finished! Total preparation time should take no more than a few minutes per recipe. You'll also learn the best ways to bottle and store your personal-care products. You won't have to worry about mixing ingredients to make shampoo each time you want to wash your hair!

PERSONAL PAMPERING MADE EASY

Ever wonder how celebrities always manage to look so fabulous? Well, maybe it's because they can afford to buy expensive products that pamper them from head to toe! But don't worry. You won't need a six-figure salary to buy yourself the same kind of care. Our recipes use simple ingredients that will yield salon-quality products for your every grooming need. For example:

Pedicure: You'll find ways to remove calluses and corns, formulas to smooth rough skin, and much more.

Manicure: Want dazzling nails without getting a fifty-dollar manicure? Here you'll find cuticle softeners, shiny nail oils, even colors you can make yourself. Also included are creams to soothe dry, rough hands.

Massage oils: Nothing relaxes tired, sore muscles and improves muscle and skin tone quite like a massage. Here you'll find easy recipes for making your own healing massage oils with natural ingredients such as eucalyptus and rosemary.

Face care: All the active, natural ingredients found in expensive eye, neck, and face creams are available in your supermarket and drugstore for less than half the price of prepackaged products. Learn how to blend fruit juices to make your own exfoliating ointments and wrinkle creams.

Tooth brighteners: Over-the-counter tooth whitening and brightening pastes are popular products for folks who want a bright, sparkling smile. But just one tube can set you back as much as fifteen dollars. Here you'll find dental-care products that yield the same results for pennies.

Hair color and highlights: Professional hair color not only costs a lot, it's also hard on your hair. You'll find recipes for hair color, lighteners, and gray concealers that will not only save you money, they will leave your hair softer and healthier.

Of course, you'll also find dozens of recipes for all the basic personal-care products you use every day, such as shampoos, soaps, and conditioners.

A Word about Safety

Just because a product is made with 100 percent natural ingredients does not mean that it's perfectly harmless. It is important that you regard your homemade personal-care products with the same caution you would any other store-bought cleanser or cosmetic.

The first rule of safety is always to perform a patch test on yourself to check for allergic reactions before using a product. To perform a patch test, simply apply a small amount of the product to the sensitive skin of your inner arm right above or below the elbow and wait for twenty-four hours. If there is no reaction, it is probably safe to proceed with the treatment. If redness, swelling, or any other form of irritation occurs, do not use the product. Because many of these recipes use fresh, unpreserved ingredients, such as fruits and vegetables, it's important that you perform a patch test each time you mix a fresh batch, even if you've used the recipe before. The strawberries you buy at the end of the season can have a very different chemical makeup and acidity from the ones you bought at the beginning. It's better to be safe than to risk an irritating allergic reaction.

Certain ingredients require more care than others. Herbs and essential oils—volatile oils that give distinctive odors, flavors, and other characteristics to plants, flowers, and fruits—are potent substances, and some people are sensitive to them. Stay on the safe side. Do not exceed the recommended amounts of ingredients. When using essential oils, do not swallow or even taste the ingredients. Keep bottles and jars sealed and out of the reach of children. Do not use essential oils without consulting your doctor if you have chronic or acute conditions such as heart disease, diabetes, epilepsy, or asthma. Young children and pregnant women shouldn't use essential oils.

Remember, your naturally made personal-care products do not contain preservatives, and so, although they have a reasonable shelf life with proper storage, it's important to check your products regularly to be certain that they haven't deteriorated. Generally speaking, store your products in cool, dark places, such as the refrigerator or a closed cupboard. Try to keep your fingers out of the product as much as possible. Instead, use cotton balls and swabs to keep the products germ-free. Before each use, check the color and odor of the product. If it's discolored or has an unusual smell, that's a sign that the ingredients have begun to break down and that you should discard the product without using it.

Finally, always label and date your personal-care products. That way you know exactly what's in that mysterious amber bottle and when you made it. Proper labeling will also help to prevent unsuspecting family members from washing their hands with face lotions or brushing their teeth with cosmetic powder!

Chapter 1

The Easy Beauty Pantry

The best way to venture into homemade personal-care products is to start with a well-stocked pantry. Most of what you need is probably already nestled away in your kitchen. There are just a few ingredients and pieces of equipment that you may not have readily available. Here are some tips for getting started.

TOOLS OF THE TRADE

This suggested list of beauty-product "tools" is not mandatory. Obviously, you can finely chop your ingredients if you don't have a coffee grinder. These items just make the process easier.

Blender: Great for mixing hand creams and lotions, which require a little more effort to blend. But a good whisk and a big glass bowl can work just as well in a pinch.

Bottles and jars: It's a good idea to have a large assortment of bottles and jars and to use containers that best fit the product. For products such as eye creams that you'll make in small doses, try to use as small a jar as possible so that the ingredients have minimal contact with air, which can hasten deterioration. Amber or other colored bottles work best to protect the products from light. Any container you use should have an airtight lid to prevent your product from evaporating or deteriorating.

Bowls: Glass or nonporous ceramic bowls are the easiest to clean. They're also less likely than metal bowls to react with any of your ingredients.

Coffee grinder: Coffee grinders and spice grinders make mincing herbs and other "flaky" ingredients a breeze. Just be sure to wash the grinder thoroughly before using it to grind coffee beans. Or, better yet, if you find yourself using your coffee grinder a lot, buy another one to use exclusively for personal-care products.

Funnel: Having a funnel on hand will make it easier to transfer ingredients from pans and mixing bowls to bottles and jars. Stainless steel is better than plastic because some essential oils can react with and damage plastic.

Grater: Perfect for gathering fine pieces of citrus peels and for making soap flakes. Any kitchen grater will do.

Knives: The same kinds of knives you use for cooking also come in handy to slice and chop ingredients for personal-care products.

Measuring cups and spoons: For the best results, it's important to use exact measurements of ingredients, rather than estimating by using regular cups and spoons. Try to use glass or stainless steel cups and stainless steel spoons, since some of the ingredients can react with aluminum and other metals.

Paper towels: Some recipes may call for straining ingredients. If you prefer, you can use cheesecloth or coffee filters, but inexpensive paper towels work just as well.

Plastic spray bottles: Many personal-care products are best applied with an atomizer or spray bottle. Drugstores carry inexpensive plastic spray bottles in a wide variety of shapes, sizes, and colors.

Pots and pans: Again, because you'll be working with some fairly reactive ingredients, you'll want to use the least reactive cooking materials available. Your best bets for pots and pans are stainless steel, glass, coated aluminum, and ironware that has been coated with enamel or another nonstick surface.

Vegetable peeler: Have one on hand for recipes that call for fruits and vegetables without the peel.

Whisk or electric mixer: For most recipes, a stainless steel whisk or a stainless steel or wooden spoon is all you need for mixing. But an electric mixer comes in handy for thicker products such as lotions and creams.

SUPER BEAUTY STAPLES

Some ingredients are just so wonderful for cleansing or moisturizing that you'll be using them again and again in shampoos, soaps, and lotions. Here are twenty personal-care product staples you should always have on hand.

Almonds: Whether you use them in a paste or as an oil, almonds are a must on your personal-care product shelves. Ripe almonds can be ground up and made into a skin-cleansing paste that also has a slight bleaching effect that smooths blotchy skin. Almond oil, long used by the Greeks to combat the dry skin caused by the hot Mediterranean sun, makes a superb moisturizer and is used frequently in lotions and creams.

Aloe vera: The healing sap of the aloe vera plant is a well-known remedy for burns, cuts, scratches, and sunburn as well as many other skin conditions. It also makes a great moisturizing skin lotion, especially in the blistering summer months and during the harsh winter season. You can buy the gel at most pharmacies, or you can grow your own aloe plant.

Avocado: Rich in essential fats and vitamins and minerals, the buttery flesh of the avocado makes a cleansing, nourishing facial product. You can use it either as an everyday facial wash or as a special dry-skin-replenishing facial mask. Keep whole fresh fruits on hand in your refrigerator.

Banana: Another fruit rich in vitamins and minerals, bananas, mashed or pureed, are perfect for quick, at-home facials. Bananas also react well with almost all skin types and are unlikely to cause allergic reactions.

Beer: Keep a couple of open bottles of beer in your refrigerator for a few days when your hair is feeling limp and lifeless. The sugar and protein found in beer help make it an excellent hair-setting and rinsing lotion that adds weight and body to your hair. But don't use the beer straight from the bottle or tap. It works better when it's flat.

Cornstarch: Used to soothe painful diaper rash in babies, cornstarch is an important ingredient for cosmetics of all kinds. Because of its superior absorbency, some people use it instead of talcum powder. It makes an excellent face-dusting powder. Home beauty recipes often call for cornstarch as a thickening agent for lotions and creams.

Cucumber: You already know that cucumbers can help ease tired, puffy eyes. But cucumbers also contain compounds that keep your hair and nails healthy and that heal damaged skin. The juice from fresh cucumbers is a useful astringent for oily skin. And cucumber juice or slices also can help cool a sunburn and restore vitality to sun-damaged summer skin.

Egg: Eggs may be one of the most versatile ingredients found in your beauty-product pantry. The fatty-acid-rich egg yolk is ideal for bringing dry skin and hair back to life when used in facials and conditioners. Egg whites, on the other hand, bring astringent relief to oily skin. They have a tightening effect on skin and can be used to temporarily reduce fine wrinkles for special occasions.

Essential oils: Highly concentrated essential oils like those found in lavender, sage, and eucalyptus play an important role in personal-care products of all kinds, especially fragrances, massage oils, hair conditioners, shampoos, and footbaths. You'll find a wide array of oils available in health-food stores. Eventually, you'll stock the ones that you use the most on your pantry shelves.

Honey: Used by the Egyptians to help embalm bodies and drunk by the Greeks as a divine nectar, honey is an excellent antiseptic, cleanser, and moisture-trapping humectant. This natural substance is used in a wide array of recipes, including those for facial masks, moisturizing baths, body lotions, and rough-skin softeners. There are dozens of varieties of honey to choose from. Simply select the one that you find the most appealing in aroma, texture, and color.

Lemon: You probably remember the power of lemon from summers of your youth when you applied it to your hair to create natural highlights. Well, this citrus fruit not only lightly bleaches your hair summer blonde, it also helps lighten freckles, remove blackheads, and fade dark patches on your skin. It's popularly used in homemade hand lotions, body rubs, and dead-skin exfoliaters. Being astringent, it's also invaluable in fighting oily skin.

Mayonnaise: Natural mayonnaise is a cornucopia of ingredients including eggs, oil, and vinegar that are great for skin and hair care. Mayonnaise nourishes, smooths, and softens skin. In fact, while it's an essential ingredient in many personal-care product recipes, mayonnaise also can be used on its own as a replacement for most expensive night creams.

Milk: Rich in essential vitamins and minerals, milk is a superior healing lotion for the skin. You can keep it stocked fresh in your refrigerator. Or, if you don't drink much milk and fear it will spoil, you can keep a carton of dried milk that can be reconstituted as you need it. Milk comes in handy for a variety of recipes, from whole-body milk baths to eye soothers to facials. Milk is especially useful for fighting dry, chapped winter skin.

Mint: This invigorating, refreshing herb shows up in a vast array of personal-care product recipes. Used medicinally and cosmetically for centuries, mint comes in a wide variety of strains, including spearmint and peppermint. The compounds found in mint are soothing, astringent, and powerfully aromatic; this herb makes a wonderful pick-me-up bath splash. Of course, mint also shows up in a host of other products, including tooth whiteners and breath fresheners.

Oatmeal: Brimming with protein, potassium, and magnesium, oatmeal is a cleanser, nourisher, and smoother and is especially good for sensitive skin. This popular breakfast cereal is so gentle and effective it can be used as a substitute for soap. It also helps heal rough skin, clears blackheads, and gently bleaches freckles and dark patches. Oatmeal also makes a popular facial mask. For the best results, buy regular oatmeal instead of the instant variety when using the cereal for personal-care products.

Olive oil: Originating in the Mediterranean, olive oil is probably one of the very first oils used in cosmetics. This rich, yellow-green oil was an important ingredient in the first cold cream, invented about 2,000 years ago, and is still used today in a wide array of skin moisturizers, lotions, hair conditioners, eye and neck wrinkle creams, and perfumes. Olive oil is not only a popular ingredient in many of these products, it also can be used straight from the bottle for intensive care of dry skin and hair.

Rosemary: This highly aromatic herb from the Mediter-ranean region was used by the ancient Romans as a medicine, a decoration, and a food flavoring. Today, it's still a popular seasoning worldwide. It also makes an excellent cosmetic ingre-dient in body, face, hair, and even dental products. Rosemary's astringent properties make it perfect as an oily-skin tonic. Some believe that inhaling the rich aroma of rosemary can relieve headaches.

Tea: Teas, both regular and herbal, are frequently used in personal-care products. Like cucumber slices, cool, wet tea bags are an excellent remedy for under-eye puffiness. Tea also is a powerful astringent, making it particularly useful for treating oily skin. Some folks even take tea baths to give their bodies healthful summertime glows during those pale winter months. You can keep your favorite tea bags on hand. Or you can buy special loose-leaf varieties that also include herbs and spices.

Vinegar: Vinegar may be one of the oldest home remedies. Your grandmother probably used it for everything from cleaning the kitchen cabinets to making a homemade douche. Well, vinegar is every bit as versatile today as it was then. White and apple cider vinegars are popular ingredients for controlling dan-druff, creating a healthy sheen on hair, removing blackheads, relieving dry-skin flakiness, and even neutralizing body secre-tions to control body odor.

Yogurt: Rich in protein, calcium, and vitamins, yogurt is a superb skin softener and can be applied directly to the face and body as a cream and moisturizer. Yogurt also is rich in lactic acids that act as a mild skin bleach to gradually fade unwanted freckles or dark patches. Keep a tub of plain yogurt in your refrigerator at all times. Or, if you're really ambitious, many natural-food cookbooks can teach you how to make your own.

PICKING PRODUCE AND OTHER INGREDIENTS

Unless a recipe specifies otherwise, the general rule of thumb is always to choose fresh ingredients whenever you can. Obviously, there will be certain times of the year, like winter, when fresh ingredients are tough to find. When using vegetables, you can get away with frozen when fresh aren't available. But because fruit doesn't freeze as well as vegetables, your best bet in a pinch may be canned fruit. If you must use canned produce, be sure to buy the kind that is canned in its natural juices with no sugar added. Also, rinse canned ingredients well before using them.

When buying herbs, you generally have the option of choosing fresh or dried. Again, if you can get them, fresh herbs are the best way to go. If you cannot get fresh herbs, dried are sufficient. If you find yourself using dried herbs much of the time, you might want to consider growing your own herbs in a little windowsill herb box. Or you could buy fresh herbs when they're available and dry them yourself, so that at least you know that the dried herbs you're using are not old and still have some kick. You can dry herbs very simply by tying them in small bunches with a string and hanging them upside down in a place that is reasonably dry and where there is circulating air.

Some recipes call for essential oils—highly concentrated extracts of the original fruit, flower, herb, or spice that have been drawn out and bottled. Because these oils are so potent, most recipes will require only small amounts. Personal-care products containing essential oils should always be shaken before use to make sure that the oil is evenly dispersed.

You can buy all other ingredients such as vegetable oils and dairy products as you normally would. Just be sure to check freshness dates before use to avoid spoiling a whole batch because of one "bad" ingredient.

It's Prep Time!

Treat the produce you use for personal-care products as carefully as you would if you were preparing dinner for your family. Always thoroughly clean and rinse fresh fruits and vegetables. Even organically grown produce is often sprayed or treated with organic pesticides, herbicides, and fungicides that you don't want getting into your soaps and lotions.

If a recipe doesn't specify that the ingredient be cooked first, you can assume it will be used raw. The same is true of the skins on fruits and vegetables. Unless the recipe asks for produce to be peeled, assume you're using the whole food, skin and all.

To make preparation quick and easy, be sure to have all of the ingredients, as well as preparation equipment, out and ready for action. We've listed the ingredients and equipment up front in each recipe.

Bottling and Storing

Since you won't be using additives and preservatives, it's important to bottle and store your personal-care products in a way that limits their exposure to air and germs so that they stay fresher longer.

Before you begin, you should wash and dry the mixing bowls, utensils, and pots and pans you'll be using. You should also sterilize all of your cosmetic bottles and jars. If you're storing products in plastic containers that can't withstand boiling temperatures, simply wash them in warm soapy water, dry them, and keep them covered until they're ready to be used. You can sterilize glass jars and containers using the following procedure:

♦ Thoroughly wash all bottles, jars, and lids inside and out in warm, soapy water. Use an old toothbrush or a bottlebrush to clean inside slim containers.

• Fill the sink with clean, warm water and rinse all containers and lids completely. Replace the water if it becomes too soapy.

• Completely submerge all jars and lids in a pot of water on the stove. (A canning pot or rack is especially helpful if you have one.) Turn the heat on high and bring the water to a boil.

• Boil the water for ten minutes. Drain the jars and place them on a clean towel until they're ready for use. Or you can take the jars directly from the pot as you need them.

Once you've poured or funneled your personal-care products into their appropriate containers, you should always label each product. Note on the label the product, the ingredients, and the day the product was made. This will save you a lot of guesswork later because without the use of dyes and artificial colors, many cosmetic products look remarkably alike. Including the date on the label also helps keep track of the product's age so that you know when it's time to make a fresh batch.

Your personal-care products will last longer if you store them away from heat, moisture, and light. Also, try to minimize their contact with air. Because all of these elements can quicken the deterioration of many ingredients, the best storage spot for most products is a cool, dark place, such as a refrigerator or a closed cabinet. When using ingredients that spoil quickly (these ingredients are noted in the recipes), try making only as much as you or your family will use in a short period of time.

WEIGHTS AND MEASUREMENTS

Expect to use the same measurements you would when baking or cooking. The following weights and measurements conversion chart will help you measure the right amounts of ingredients.

3 teaspoons	=	1 tablespoon
4 tablespoons	=	1/4 cup
8 tablespoons	=	1/2 cup
1 cup	=	8 ounces
1 cup	=	1/2 pint
2 cups	=	1 pint
4 cups	=	1 quart
2 pints	=	1 quart
2 quarts	=	1/2 gallon
4 quarts	=	1 gallon
1 pound	=	16 ounces

Chapter 2

Beautiful Skin

Ancient beauties like Cleopatra deserve a lot of credit. Although they lived in an age before beauty salons, wrinkle creams, and cosmetics, they still managed to come up with natural beauty formulas that made their skin soft, smooth, and supple. Cleopatra, in fact, may be one of the forerunners of state-of-the-art skin care. This Egyptian beauty developed a milk bath famed for diminishing wrinkles and for promoting baby-soft skin. (Julius Caesar and Marc Antony would attest to its success!) Today we know that milk contains alpha hydroxy acids (AHAs), which are used in anti-aging creams sold all over the world.

In this section, you'll learn how to treat yourself like a queen by making your very own milk bath. You'll also find recipes for interesting bath formulas, soaps, shower gels, body scrubs, moisturizers, and other special treatments. These recipes rely on all-natural ingredients, which means that your skin will get the best care the earth has to offer. And as a bonus, your wallet will be bulging with the hundreds of dollars you have not spent on expensive skin products!

SOOTHING BATHS

Among the most popular treatments on the roster at health spas are baths. There may be nothing more soothing to your skin or relaxing for your mind than a warm herbal bath. Depending on the bath formula you use, your soak can relieve dry skin, tone oily skin, or keep normal skin its healthy best. Baths also can help wake you in the morning or put you to sleep at night. Here are a few favorite bath formulas.

THE DIVINE SOAK

In ancient Greece, milk and honey were fabled to be the food of the gods. Well, they're also great for your skin. Honey is rich in minerals as well as vitamin C and the good-for-your-skin B-complex vitamins. These elements help moisturize, nourish, and soften skin. Milk, chock-full of alpha hydroxy acids, can help exfoliate dead skin cells, exposing the young-looking skin below. Together, they make a heavenly bath.

Ingredients
2   cups milk
1/2 cup honey
1   tablespoon fresh mint
1   tablespoon baking soda

Combine ingredients in mixing bowl. With electric mixer or whisk, blend for about sixty seconds. Pour into glass jar. Makes enough for about two baths—one cup per bath. Pour directly into bathwater while tub is filling.

Storage and life span: Store in a covered container in the refrigerator. This mixture will stay good for about two days.

LULLABY BATH

The fragrant lavender herb contains sedative compounds that can penetrate the skin. Chamomile also is a sedative and is especially good for calming the nerves. What better way to end a stressful day than by taking a delightfully relaxing lavender-chamomile bath? As added benefits, chamomile helps to cleanse pores, and lavender helps to soothe tense and tired muscles.

Ingredients
- $1/2$ cup dried lavender (or 1 cup fresh herb)
- $1/2$ cup dried chamomile (or 1 cup fresh herb)

There are several ways to use herbs in your bath. You can throw the fresh herbs directly into your hot bathwater. Or you can put the herbs in a tea ball, nylon stocking, or other type of container that serves as a sieve so that you won't have herb flakes lining your bathtub when you drain the water.

Storage and life span: Fresh herbs dry out in a very short time. Of course, you can use dried herbs, too. Dried herbs have a shelf life of several months, but over time they lose the active ingredients that make them potent. As a rule of thumb, the less fragrant an herb is, the less potent it will be. For best results, store your herbs in airtight, dark-colored glass containers in a cool, dark place.

ROSEMARY BUBBLE BATH

Remember your first bubble bath? Remember that creamy,
bubbly water up to your chin? Now you can relive the childlike
wonder of soaking in a rich, foamy bubble bath without the
harsh detergents used in commercial formulas that can be hard
on your skin. Instead, add a rich, fragrant herb like rosemary
that not only smells heavenly, it also works as a light astringent
to tone your skin while you soak.

Ingredients

$1^1/2$ cups water
3   tablespoons dried rosemary (or 6 tablespoons fresh herb)
$1^1/2$ cups generic baby shampoo

Bring water to boil on top of stove. Place rosemary in glass bowl
or jar. When water is boiling, remove from stove and pour over
herb. Let steep for about fifteen minutes. Strain water into
another bowl. Add baby shampoo. Mix well and pour into old
shampoo bottle or other plastic container. Shake well before
using. While bathtub is filling, pour about $1/4$ cup of mixture
directly under tap into tub. Makes about three cups, or enough
for about a dozen baths.

Storage and life span: Store the mixture in a cool, dry place.
Will last for about three or four months.

SQUEAKY CLEAN VINEGAR BATH

If you have soapy film, sticky suntan lotion, or any other unwanted residue on your skin, this vinegar bath is the way to rinse it squeaky clean. Vinegar also neutralizes body odor, so you'll smell fresh and clean, too. Because vinegar creates an acidic environment that kills many harmful bacteria, a vinegar bath also is a good choice for women who are prone to yeast infections (remember the old vinegar douches?). Adding a little basil makes this bath a fragrant deep-cleansing treat.

Ingredients
- 3 cups apple cider vinegar
- 3 cups water
- 2 teaspoons dried basil (or 4 teaspoons fresh herb)

Combine all ingredients in pan and heat on stove top until boiling. Turn heat to low and simmer for about ten minutes. Strain mixture into jar or plastic container. Use about two cups per bath. Makes enough for three baths.

Storage and life span: Store in a cool, dry place. Should last for three or four months.

SIMPLE SOAPS

Soap may be the oldest personal-care product we use today. Long before the days of commercial cleansers, people would cook up a batch of lye, fat, and other ingredients to make the first bars of soap. You could do that today, too, but lye is extremely harsh, and making soap from scratch is a tough task requiring lots of equipment and a good deal of practice. Instead, if you want to create your own fragrant bath bars, like the kinds sold in specialty stores, you might want to begin with pure soap flakes and add your own ingredients. In the long run, it's cheaper than buying special soaps—and more personal, too.

Old Sage Soap

Sage is used around the world for toothpastes, hair colors, and deodorants. This fragrant herb also is believed to have healing powers and to be rich in antioxidants. In your bath, sage is the perfect herb for soothing sore muscles. It is especially good for cleansing oily skin.

Ingredients
1 1/4 cups boiling water
8 ounces pure soap flakes
2 1/2 tablespoons dried sage

In large glass or ceramic bowl, combine boiling water, soap flakes, and sage. Allow mixture to cool enough so that you can scoop up handfuls and shape them into small or large soap balls. You can flatten them to make soap "cakes," or you can leave them as pretty rounds of soap. Once they're shaped, place them on a sheet of wax paper to cool and harden.

Storage and life span: Store unused soap cakes in a cool, dark place. If stored properly, your soap should last indefinitely.

TROPICAL COCONUT SOAP

Residents of those hot, sun-drenched countries along the equator know full well that coconut oil is their skin's salvation. Rich in natural fatty acids, coconut oil is a wonderful skin softener and conditioner, especially for people who have naturally dry skin or who spend a lot of time outside in the sun or wind. As an added bonus, coconut oil increases the sudsing action of soap so that you get a richer, creamier lather.

Ingredients
1 1/4   cups boiling water
  8   ounces pure soap flakes
  2   tablespoons coconut oil

In large glass or ceramic bowl, combine boiling water, soap flakes, and coconut oil. Stir until smooth. Allow to cool. Shape soap mixture into golf-ball-sized soap rounds. Allow them to cool and harden on sheet of wax paper.

Storage and life span: Store unused soap cakes in a cool, dark place. If stored properly, your soap should last indefinitely.

WAKE-UP SHOWER WASHES AND GELS

Shower gels and body washes have taken the cosmetics industry by storm in recent years. And with good reason because consumers are finding these products to be more practical and less messy than regular bath bar soap. You, too, can make invigorating washes and gels that will soothe your skin with natural exfoliaters and moisturizers, boost your energy with invigorating fragrances, and leave you feeling squeaky clean. And they cost less than the name brands you would buy at the drugstore.

THYME-WINE BODY WASH

White wine has been used cosmetically for centuries. Its antibiotic qualities make it great for washing away germs, and it's also a light astringent, which can help control oily skin. Thyme is an ancient medicinal herb, long used for soothing stomachaches and respiratory ailments. This warm, fragrant herb also is an excellent source of thymol, which makes it a powerful antiseptic as well as a deodorant. Together these two ingredients make an excellent body wash.

Ingredients
1   handful dried thyme leaves
2   cups white wine

Simmer thyme leaves in white wine for twenty minutes. Strain and discard leaves. Pour into plastic squirt bottle (the kind bicyclists carry works best). Rub over body during shower.

Storage and life span: Store the mixture for easy access in the bathroom. Make more as necessary. Long shelf life.

HONEY-MINT GEL

Rich with B-complex vitamins, honey is an excellent way to nourish, moisturize, and soften your skin. It's especially useful for healing dry, cracked skin. Cool, refreshing mint is a stimulant, perfect for reviving skin and muscles still tired from a night's sleep. Mint also is a light astringent and will remove that fine layer of oil that accumulates on your skin overnight. Together, these two make a shower gel that will leave your skin clean, soft, and invigorated.

Ingredients

    2   cups water
3 1/2   tablespoons finely chopped fresh spearmint
1 1/2   tablespoons honey
1 1/2   tablespoons baking soda

Bring water to boil in pan. Pour boiling water over mint in glass jar. Let steep for ten minutes. Strain minty water into mixing bowl. Add remaining ingredients and stir. Pour into plastic or liquid soap bottle. Use as liquid soap in shower. The ingredients will separate while sitting, so shake well before each use. Keep near shower for easy access.

Storage and life span: For best results, this mixture should be used within a week.

Raspberry Delight Shower Gel

This is a perfect summertime shower gel. Raspberries, naturally cooling to the body, have a light acidic content that tones and exfoliates sun- and summer-drenched skin. And they smell delightful! The little bit of tea in this recipe also is a perfect summer-skin saver. Tea helps heal sunburns, and it leaves skin shimmering and glowing.

Ingredients
- 1 quart boiling water
- 4 raspberry herbal tea bags
- 1 cup pure soap flakes

Bring two pints (half the water) to boil in pan on stove. Add tea bags, remove from heat, and let steep for five minutes. While tea bags are steeping, pour other half of water in another pan along with soap flakes. Warm over low heat until soap has dissolved. (Do not let water begin to simmer.) Once flakes are dissolved, add raspberry tea and continue to stir until formula is evenly mixed. Pour mixture into large plastic bottle and allow it to set into soft soap.

Storage and life span: Store in a cool, dark place. For best results, use within several months.

The Simplest Shower Gel

Nothing is as fragrant or as soothing as a rose, whose aroma carries you back to simpler times and endless summer days. Now, you can make a two-step shower gel that will wrap you in the sweet smell of roses every morning. Although this recipe "cheats" a little bit in that it uses some commercial soap, it's much too satisfying to pass up, and it's still less expensive to make than to buy at a specialty shop.

Ingredients

2   cups unscented, dye-free liquid soap
15-20 drops rose essential oil

Pour liquid soap into bowl and mix in rose oil, a couple of drops at a time, until fragrance is as strong or as light as you desire. Then pour mixture into container (pump-style plastic bottles work best). Keep near shower for easy access.

Storage and life span: This product keeps very well. It will last as long as any liquid soap.

ALL-OVER MOISTURIZERS

You know how soft and smooth a baby's skin feels. That's because it's still rich in natural oils and supple and flexible enough to bounce back from smiles and tears and other facial movements. As we age, our skin starts to lose that elasticity. It becomes rough around the edges and fine lines begin to show. And that's where moisturizers come in. They won't take wrinkles away, but they will lessen the appearance of those fine lines as well as protect skin against heat, wind, cold, and other harmful environmental elements. Moisturizers are best applied immediately after showering.

SUNNY SUNFLOWER MOISTURIZER

This delightful combination of sunflower oil, peanut oil, and lemon juice is perfect for leaving skin fresh, clean, and supple following a bath or shower. Sunflower oil is rich in vitamin E, which nourishes the skin. Peanut oil is rich in fatty acids and makes an excellent skin lubricant. It's especially good for those thin-skinned areas around the neck and elbows. Lemon juice is a wonderful skin cleanser and is great for removing dirt from pores.

Ingredients
    5   tablespoons sunflower oil
    3   tablespoons peanut oil
    4   tablespoons lemon juice

Combine ingredients in small pan. Stir over medium heat until well blended. Pour into small bottle, such as a spray bottle or a suntan-lotion bottle. Keep near shower or sink and apply after showering.

Storage and life span: Can be stored at room temperature. Best if used within seven to ten days.

Nut 'n' Honey Lotion

As the ancient Greeks knew, honey is wonderful for your skin. Brimming with B vitamins and trace minerals, it softens and nourishes weather-beaten skin. Cocoa butter and oil from the coconut act as emollients, which means they soothe and soften skin. High in saturated fat, coconut oil is particularly good for lubricating and protecting skin from the elements, which is why it is such a popular ingredient in suntan lotions—that, and it smells so good!

Ingredients

- 1/8 teaspoon borax powder
- 1/4 cup water
- 1/2 cup coconut oil
- 1 tablespoon grated cocoa butter
- 1 teaspoon honey

Dissolve borax powder in water in small, heat-resistant glass bowl. Set aside. In another heat-resistant saucepan or bowl, combine coconut oil, cocoa butter, and honey. Gently heat oil and cocoa butter until melted together. The best way to do this is to boil about two inches of water in larger pan and place bowl with oil and cocoa butter on top of that pan. When oil and cocoa butter have combined, bring water-borax mixture to boil (either in microwave or on stove top). Remove oil-cocoa butter mixture from stove and gradually add borax-water, using whisk to blend thoroughly. Allow to cool completely. Pour lotion into airtight dispenser.

Storage and life span: Makes about eight ounces and will last as long as commercial moisturizers do.

ALMOND-SAFFLOWER SKIN SOOTHER

Mediterranean women, long known for their smooth, silky skin, have relied on the restorative power of almond oil for centuries. Almonds contain skin-nourishing vitamin E, and their oil is ideal for combating the dryness caused by sun and wind. Safflower oil also is rich in fatty acids and provides a second layer of protection. Equal measures of lemon and lime juice will make your skin sparkle.

Ingredients
    2   teaspoons almond oil
    2   teaspoons safflower oil
    2   teaspoons lemon juice
    2   teaspoons lime juice

Heat ingredients over medium-high heat in small saucepan. Let cool and then pour into small spray bottle. Apply by spraying on and rubbing into skin. Shake well before every application, since oils and juices will separate.

Storage and life span: Store at room temperature. For best results, use within seven to ten days.

ALOE-CHAMOMILE GEL

Aloe may be the queen of plants when it comes to healing sunburned or weather-beaten skin. Chamomile adds a delightful scent to this moisturizer. In addition, the herb can help reduce skin puffiness. You could make this recipe with the oil from your own aloe plant, but it would be a lot of work for very little product. Better to just pick up some pure aloe vera gel at your drugstore.

Ingredients
   1   cup aloe vera gel
   2   tablespoons dried chamomile flowers

Combine ingredients in heat-resistant bowl. Place bowl in saucepan containing about two inches of boiling water (like double boiler). Heat until liquefied and chamomile flowers infuse into gel. Remove from heat and allow to cool. Strain fragrant gel into lotion dispenser.

Storage and life span: Store in a cool, dark place. Will last as long as any commercial lotion.

Chapter 3

The Pampered Face

If you added up the cost of all the personal-care products you buy, then divided them into "face" products and "other," you'd find that about 80 percent of creams, lotions, cleansers, bracers, and cosmetics are intended for your face. Little wonder, really, when you consider how important your face is. Even in the dead of winter, when the rest of your body is well under wraps, your face is hanging out there for all the world to see.

Naturally, since our faces get all the exposure, they also get the lion's share of attention and protection. We want them to look nice, and we'd like to keep them that way. Unfortunately, that can mean countertops full of expensive products that may or may not work as well as we'd like. Again, the best solution can be those beauty products you make yourself.

Natural facial cleansers, moisturizers, and masks have a rich tradition in history. Ancient Egyptians used milk, fruit juices, and mud and clay baths to exfoliate dead cells and to revive tender facial skin weathered by hours in the desert sun. European women used eggs and cucumbers to keep their complexions youthful and vibrant. Women all around the globe have understood the power of flowers, herbs, and fresh foods to keep facial skin at its pampered best. Why else would so many major cosmetic companies rely on these natural ingredients for their products?

Following is a host of recipes for scrubs, cleansers, masks, and other facial skin-care products that should help all skin types.

START-THE-DAY-SPLASHES

Let's face it, when Monday morning rolls around, we often feel a little more weary than relaxed from the busy weekend behind us, a fact that's written all over our tired faces. But instead of waiting for puffy eyes to deflate and dull skin to achieve its normal glow, you can quickly invigorate your face with a splash. These lively splashes contain ingredients such as wine and vinegar that tone skin and fresh herbs that add nourishment and a wonderful fragrance.

CHAMOMILE A.M. SPLASH

Native to western Europe and western North Africa, chamomile is a cleansing, toning herb that can help clear pores and reduce skin puffiness. The apple cider vinegar in this recipe is an excellent treatment for all skin types because it helps maintain the skin's normal protective coating. No worries about smelling "vinegary" with this recipe, either. The chamomile flowers create a wonderful aroma.

Ingredients

1 cup apple cider vinegar
3 teaspoons dried chamomile flowers
2 quarts springwater or filtered water

Bring vinegar to simmer on stove top. Add dried flowers. Turn heat to low and allow to steep for fifteen minutes. Strain mixture into half-gallon container. Add water until container is almost full. Shake well. Pour some splash into sport-type squirt bottle for use in bathroom. Store rest of mixture in cool, dark place, such as a refrigerator. Splash liberal amounts on face, as desired. Avoid splashing directly into eyes.

Storage and life span: If stored properly, this product should last for several months.

"Witchy" Spearmint Wake Up

The herb witch hazel has been used for centuries to heal skin ailments of all kinds, from burns, bites, and scratches to varicose veins and dandruff. It's also a popular ingredient in facial cosmetics. Because witch hazel is an astringent, it is particularly useful for stripping away oil that accumulates in your pores overnight. The cooling tingle of spearmint adds a refreshing wake-up call to this mixture. In addition, mint acts as a light astringent, and so it is useful for clearing up a "greasy" morning face. A touch of honey helps maintain moisture.

Ingredients
- 2/3 cup filtered water or springwater
- 1 teaspoon dried spearmint (or 1 tablespoon fresh herb)
- 1/2 cup witch hazel
- 1–2 drops honey

Bring water to boil on stove. Remove from heat and mix in mint. Cover and allow to steep for ten to fifteen minutes. Strain mint infusion and mix in other ingredients. Pour blended product into squirt bottle and keep by bathroom sink.

Storage and life span: Will last for several months.

Morning Wine Breezer

White wine is perfect for tired morning skin. Lightly astringent, it helps clear oil- and dirt-clogged pores. It also works as an antiseptic so that you're certain to start the day with a fresh, clean face. Raspberries have an invigorating, cooling effect on the skin—especially during those sun-baked summer months. Their lightly acidic content will help flush away dead skin cells and enhance your naturally supple complexion.

Ingredients

1 teaspoon dried raspberry leaves
(or raspberry herbal tea leaves)
2 cups white wine

Simmer raspberry leaves in white wine for twenty minutes. Strain and then discard leaves. Pour into plastic squirt bottle. Apply liberally to face as desired.

Storage and life span: Store the mixture for easy access in the bathroom. Long shelf life.

MASKS

Facial masks serve many beautifying purposes. On the most basic level, they tighten skin and pores as they dry, squeezing out blackheads so that your skin emerges clean and healthy. Old-time mud masks are perfect for this purpose. But masks can be taken to even higher levels by adding herbs, fruits, vegetables, and other natural food products that also nourish, moisturize, and tone skin. You can choose from a wide array of ingredients to best suit your skin type. Masks are most effective on freshly washed skin.

SIMPLE EGG MASK

Here's a recipe that some professional beauticians advise using right before a party or event where you really want your complexion to be perfect. All you need are egg whites, which act as an astringent to lightly remove excess oil from the skin. The eggs also temporarily tighten skin so that pores appear smaller and fine lines are diminished.

Ingredients
1–2   egg whites (use 1 if large eggs, 2 if small)

Separate whites in mixing bowl. With fork or whisk, beat whites until frothy. Apply directly to face, avoiding eyes and lips. Allow to sit for twenty minutes. Rinse face well with warm water and pat dry.

Storage and life span: Use entire mixture in one application.

Sunny Avocado Mask

For centuries, Mediterranean women have used the precious oils from avocados to keep their sun-drenched skin smooth and supple. Avocados are rich in monounsaturated fat—the kind found in olive oil—and other fatty acids. Sunflower oil is an excellent source of skin-healing vitamin E. Together these ingredients make a mask that's a lifesaver for anyone who suffers from dry or weather-chapped skin.

Ingredients
- 1 medium avocado, mashed
- 2 tablespoons sunflower oil

Mash avocado in bowl. Add sunflower oil. Continue to mash until oil is evenly blended with avocado and you have a smooth, creamy mixture. Apply to entire face. Allow to sit for twenty minutes. Rinse face well with warm water and then pat skin dry.

Storage and life span: The high fat and oil content of this mask make it unsuitable for storage. Use the entire mixture in one application.

YOGURT-OATMEAL MASK

Oatmeal is brimming with essential ingredients that nourish your skin, including protein, potassium, magnesium, and iron. It is an extremely soothing substance that helps heal dry, flaky skin. As a bonus, oatmeal has a slight bleaching action and will help even out patchy, sun-spotted complexions. Yogurt contains lactic acid, which exfoliates rough, dead skin cells. It also acts as a light bleach.

Ingredients

1/2 cup cooked oatmeal
(whole oats rather than instant oatmeal work best)
1/4 cup plain yogurt

Mix cooled, cooked oatmeal in bowl with yogurt. Stir until ingredients are well blended. Spread mixture evenly on face, avoiding hairline. Allow to sit for about fifteen to twenty minutes. Rinse face thoroughly with warm water and then pat dry.

Storage and life span: This mask will not store well because the oatmeal will dry out. Use in one application only. If you have too much left over, simply cut down the recipe the next time.

SUMMERTIME FRUIT MASK

Fresh summertime fruits are perfect for after-sun facial care. The fruit acids lift dry, dead skin cells that could otherwise leave you with dry, patchy skin. Vitamins such as A, B, and C help keep skin healthy and glowing. Fruit juices are cool and invigorating, and they smell absolutely delicious. And as you become more comfortable with making masks, you can experiment by substituting some of your favorite summertime fruits.

Ingredients

- $1/4$ cup sliced strawberries
- $1/4$ cup raspberries
- $1/4$ cup diced cantaloupe
- 2 tablespoons honey

In mixing bowl, combine strawberries, raspberries, and cantaloupe. Lightly mash until coarsely blended. Add honey. Continue lightly mashing until mixture is well blended and sticky. Apply evenly to entire face. Allow to sit for fifteen to twenty minutes. Rinse face thoroughly with warm water and then pat dry.

Storage and life span: This mixture is best used fresh, as fruits will brown and separate if stored for more than a few hours. Use entire mixture in one application.

Banana-Honey Mask

Bananas are the universal skin soother. Rich in potassium and vitamin C, bananas are wonderful moisturizers and humectants (moisture trappers). They're also acceptable for practically everybody because they are highly nonallergenic. Honey acts as a cleanser, conditioner, and moisturizer. Together these ingredients leave your skin feeling rich, supple, and smooth.

Ingredients
   1/2 medium banana
   2 tablespoons honey

Mash banana in mixing bowl. Add honey. Continue mashing until honey and banana are well blended. Apply over entire face. Allow to sit for fifteen to twenty minutes. Rinse face well with warm water and pat dry.

Storage and life span: Mashed banana does not keep well. Use entire mixture in one application.

SCRUBS AND CLEANSERS

As we age, that layer of dead skin on our epidermis seems to get thicker and thicker, leaving us with dry, rough skin that can look blotchy and tough. That's why facial and body scrubs leave our skin with such a beautiful glow. They gently exfoliate that hard, dead layer, leaving young, fresh, soft skin exposed for all the world to see. Generally, body scrubs are necessary only once or twice a week. And no matter how often we wash our faces, our complexions occasionally need a really thorough cleansing to remove those dead cells that block our pores and give our skin an uneven, ruddy appearance. If we're very active, spend a lot of time outdoors, or live in a city environment where pollution is prevalent, it's a good idea to treat our skin to a deep cleansing about twice a week.

STRAWBERRY-HONEY SCRUB

Fresh strawberries make an ideal facial scrub. Strawberry juice is an astringent, cleanser, and conditioner all at once. The fruit also is rich in skin-nourishing vitamin C and potassium. And while the juice is performing all those duties, the tiny strawberry seeds are busy lifting and removing dead cells from the skin's surface, allowing the juice to penetrate even further. Adding a touch of honey to the fruit adds extra conditioning, moisturizing, and softening action to this facial scrub.

Ingredients
- 3 large fresh strawberries
- 2 tablespoons honey

Mash strawberries in small mixing bowl. Add honey and continue mashing until well blended. Apply mixture to face by rubbing in circular motions with pads of fingertips. Rub entire face, then rinse well with warm water. Pat skin dry.

Storage and life span: Can be kept in refrigerator for two days. But it's best if made fresh before each application.

SESAME SCRUB

Sesame seeds are among the oldest of the home-beauty ingredients. Rich in vitamin E and monounsaturated oils, sesame oil is nourishing to the skin and acts as a moisturizer and an emollient, leaving the skin with a smooth, silky appearance. Mixing whole sesame seeds into the recipe helps remove dead surface skin and nourishes the youthful skin below.

Ingredients
1/4 cup sesame oil
 1 teaspoon sesame seeds

Mix oil and seeds together in small mixing bowl until seeds are evenly distributed within mixture. Using pads of fingertips, apply blend to entire face in circular motion. Rinse face thoroughly with warm water. Pat skin dry.

Storage and life span: Sesame seeds are high in fat and go rancid quickly. Store mixture in refrigerator and discard after two days.

Sweet Milk Scrub

Famed beauties Cleopatra and Marie Antoinette are believed to have included milk-based cleansers in their arsenal of cosmetic secrets. Today we know that milk is rich in lactic acid, which helps lift and remove dead skin cells from the surface of our faces, diminishing fine wrinkles and exposing youthful skin. Here we add a spoonful of sugar to aid the exfoliating action and to stimulate the skin, resulting in a radiant glow.

Ingredients

2–3 tablespoons fresh whole milk
  1 teaspoon white sugar

Pour milk into small, shallow dish. Add sugar and blend until sugar begins to soften and dissolve. Using pads of fingertips, apply blend to entire face in gentle circular motion. Rinse well with warm water and pat skin dry.

Storage and life span: This milk and sugar blend does not keep well. Use in one application.

SENSITIVE-SKIN SCRUB

Some people's skin is too sensitive for scrubs made with ground seeds. If you find these too abrasive, you can make an equally effective exfoliater out of wheat germ. Very high in fat, wheat germ is softer than most scrubs. It also is rich in vitamin E and makes an excellent skin conditioner. Add honey to this mixture and you have a gentle, nourishing body scrub you can use on even the most sensitive skin.

Ingredients
  2 cups honey
  1 cup wheat germ

Combine ingredients until wheat germ is well blended with honey. Use one or two handfuls and rub all over skin while in shower. Be sure to stir well before each use because ingredients will separate somewhat during storage.

Storage and life span: Because wheat germ is high in fat, it spoils rather quickly. For best results, store the mixture in an airtight container in the refrigerator. Use within a week.

OATMEAL-SUNFLOWER BODY SCRUB

Oatmeal is a classic beauty-spa staple used for both facials and full-body treatments. This popular cereal grain gently exfoliates dead skin cells, nourishes new skin, bleaches dark patches, and helps clean pores. Sunflower seeds are brimming with healing vitamin E and are rich in moisturizing oil. This body scrub will leave your skin feeling spa-pampered.

Ingredients

1/2 cup finely ground oatmeal
1/2 cup finely ground sunflower seeds (preshelled)

If ingredients are not already finely ground, you can use a coffee grinder to blend into fine powder. Then place mixture in airtight plastic container. When you want to use, pour small amount into your hand, add water to make pasty, and lightly rub over your skin.

Storage and life span: Sunflower seeds contain a high amount of oil, so they can spoil if left out. For best results, store the powder in the refrigerator when not in use. Use within a week.

MEDITERRANEAN CLEANSER

Lemon juice is a natural exfoliater, toner, astringent, and oil remover popularly used in masks, scrubs, and hair products. Olive oil is a moisturizing and conditioning ingredient rich in essential vitamins and fatty acids. Together these two leave your face feeling squeaky clean and well conditioned. Because lemon juice is such an effective exfoliating ingredient on its own, there is no need for a "scrubbing" agent in this recipe. If you're working with especially tough, weather-beaten skin, however, you can add a pinch of grated lemon rind to help remove stubborn dead skin cells.

Ingredients

1 tablespoon lemon juice
1 tablespoon olive oil

In small mixing bowl, combine lemon juice and olive oil. Quickly mix ingredients together using whisk or fork. Apply immediately (product will separate quickly) using gentle circular motions with fingertips. Cover entire face and then rinse well with warm water. Pat skin dry.

Storage and life span: Keep in refrigerator. Will last from seven to ten days.

Lemon-Oil Cleanser

This one is great for combination skin that is dry and rough and oily all at the same time. Its base is olive oil, which, when mixed with warm water, moistens and softens skin, helping to prevent wrinkles. It also includes a splash of lemon and a handful of sesame seeds, so it acts as a light astringent and exfoliater, stripping away dirty oils and dead skin that can clog pores and leave skin dull.

Ingredients

   1   cup olive oil
  1/2 lemon, juice from (about 3 tablespoons lemon juice)
  1/4 cup sesame seeds

Mix ingredients in glass or ceramic bowl until blended evenly. Transfer ingredients to airtight plastic container. Rub one or two handfuls over skin while showering.

Storage and life span: Sesame seeds are high in fat, making them susceptible to spoiling. For best results, keep the mixture in the refrigerator when not in use. Use within a week.

WRINKLE RELIEF

When we enter this world, our skin is incredibly smooth, soft, and supple. But years of exposure to the sun, wind, and cold and years spent laughing and crying and talking and frowning definitely leave their marks. As we get older, we end up with fine lines and wrinkles because the elasticity of our skin breaks down. Instead of snapping back after a big yawn or broad smile, it begins to form little creases. Fine lines can be considered a sign of a life well lived, but most of us would rather do without them. And while commercial "wrinkle creams" can cost a small fortune, they also can yield questionable results. On the other hand, natural products will help diminish the fine lines we already have and prevent new ones from forming—and they cost a lot less!

CHAMOMILE-SUNFLOWER SMOOTHER

Popularly used to treat upset stomachs and minor bouts with insomnia, chamomile also heals and soothes skin. This fragrant herb also reduces skin puffiness and helps remove dirt and oil from pores. Sunflower oil is rich in skin-nourishing vitamin E and fatty acids. It works as an emollient, meaning it conditions and softens skin, leaving it with a slightly silky protective covering.

Ingredients
- 1 cup water
- 1 heaping teaspoon chamomile tea
- 1/4 cup sunflower oil

Bring water to boil on stove top. Remove from heat and add chamomile. Allow to steep for ten to fifteen minutes. Strain tea into four small plastic lotion bottles (travel shampoo bottles work well). Add one tablespoon of sunflower oil to each bottle.

Keep one bottle in bathroom. Store other three in refrigerator. Shake well before applying.

Storage and life span: Using small bottles helps minimize the chamomile's exposure to air, which helps maintain the herb's active ingredients. Will last for several months.

OLD-FASHIONED EMOLLIENT

This is a remedy used by generation after generation of mothers and grandmothers. The egg in this recipe brings relief to wrinkled skin on two levels. First, the egg yolk is rich in proteins that nourish and condition dry skin and help minimize the appearance of fine lines. Second, egg whites tighten skin, leaving a smoother-looking complexion. The corn oil adds a dash of vitamin E, which gives skin a silky finish, and the apple cider vinegar helps restore the skin's pH (acid/alkaline) balance.

Ingredients
    1   egg
1 1/3   cups corn oil
        (have oil ready to pour in liquid measuring cup)
  2/3   cup apple cider vinegar

In large mixing bowl, add egg and 1/3 cup oil. Using hand mixer (or blender) begin blending both ingredients. Keep mixer going while slowly adding another 1/3 cup oil. While still mixing ingredients, add half of vinegar. Continue blending and add all but a few tablespoons of remaining oil. Add remaining vinegar while still mixing. Finally, pour in last bit of oil. You should end up with white, creamy mixture very much like mayonnaise. Rub light amounts on face morning or night.

Storage and life span: Store mixture in an airtight container in the refrigerator. Will last for about two weeks.

TROPICAL DELIGHT

Cocoa butter has long been a favorite for keeping the skin of those living on tropical islands rich and smooth. It makes an exceptional moisturizer and, if used regularly, can help prevent fine lines and creases from forming on the delicate face and neck skin. Almond oil was probably first used by the ancient Greeks to protect their complexions from the hot Mediterranean sun. Combined in this recipe, these ingredients provide a double whammy against wrinkles.

Ingredients
1/4 pound cocoa butter
1/8 cup almond oil

Grate cocoa butter into heat-resistant bowl. Bring about two inches of water to boil in shallow saucepan. Place bowl in boiling water. When cocoa butter has melted, slowly add almond oil. Heat on low and whip ingredients with whisk until they are well blended. Remove from heat and pour into cosmetic-cream jar. Allow mixture to cool before using. Apply day or night.

Storage and life span: Store in a cool, dark place. Will last for several months.

OILY SKIN REPAIR

On the one hand, people with oily skin are blessed that they don't have to combat dry skin and all the beauty problems, such as flaky skin, fine lines, and rough complexions, that come with it. On the other hand, folks with oily skin have problems all their own, particularly pores that become clogged and a complexion that shines just a little too much. The following simple products cost only pennies to make and can keep even the oiliest of skins clean and fresh.

CUCUMBER REFRESHER

As you can tell if you walk down the facial-mask aisle in any drugstore, cucumbers and skin go well together. As a light astringent, this versatile vegetable is particularly useful for oily skin because it removes unwanted oil while maintaining the skin's delicate pH (acid/alkaline) balance. The apple cider vinegar and lemon juice in this recipe provide an extra exfoliating, degreasing punch.

Ingredients

- 1 peeled, sliced cucumber
- 1 tablespoon apple cider vinegar
- 1/2 teaspoon lemon juice

Put cucumber in blender (juicer is even better) and set on high until cucumber is liquefied. Using fine sieve or cheesecloth to catch pulp, pour cucumber-juice mixture into small bowl. Add apple cider vinegar and lemon juice. Mix well with whisk. Transfer ingredients to sport-type squirt bottle. Apply by splashing onto face or by saturating fresh cotton ball and patting on skin.

Storage and life span: Because cucumber does not hold up well, store in the refrigerator and discard after two to three days.

VODKA TONIC

No, this isn't the popular mixed drink; it's an astringent for oily skin. Made from distilled potatoes or grains, vodka makes a wonderfully clear, clean oil remover. Pineapple is a refreshing exfoliater as well as a skin softener. Together the two help to eliminate unwanted oils while leaving the skin soft, smooth, and revitalized.

Ingredients
1/4 cup vodka
1/4 cup water
1 teaspoon pineapple juice

Mix vodka, water, and pineapple juice in small sport-type squirt bottle (the kind bicyclists use). Pour small amount into palm of hand and splash over face, being careful not to get any in your eyes (vodka can sting). Also can be applied with fresh cotton ball. Use every morning or whenever you feel need for quick face cleaning. Shake before using.

Storage and life span: Store in the refrigerator. Will last for six to eight weeks.

TOMATO-LIME RELIEF

The acidic tomato can bring needed relief to oily or greasy skin. The tomato not only helps restore healthy acid levels to oily skin, it also helps tone skin and improves circulation. A splash of lime juice adds an astringent, exfoliating punch to this recipe. Those with very oily skin can use it every day. Otherwise, a couple of times a week should be sufficient.

Ingredients

1 large tomato, quartered
1 teaspoon lime juice

Place tomato chunks in blender and puree until liquefied. Using fine sieve or cheesecloth to catch pulp, pour tomato juice into small mixing bowl. Add lime juice. Use whisk to mix ingredients. Transfer to sport-type squirt bottle. Apply to face with fingertips or clean cotton ball. Allow to sit two to three minutes. Rinse face with warm water and pat skin dry.

Storage and life span: Store in the refrigerator and keep no longer than two or three days.

DRY-SKIN REMEDIES

For some people, dry skin is a seasonal condition. The dry, itchy flakes come when the first autumn leaves fall and depart when the daffodils begin to bloom. For others it's a more permanent state. Either way, you could drop a small fortune in protective creams and lotions trying to keep dry skin at bay. But now, using a few simple ingredients you're likely to have at home, you can relieve dry skin quickly, simply, and inexpensively.

SUNFLOWER-LAVENDER OIL

Lavender has numerous healing properties and can act as an antiseptic for chapped, dry skin. As a bonus, this aromatic herb acts as a mild sedative, its fragrance soothing and relaxing. Sunflower oil is brimming with vitamin E, a well-known skin nourisher and replenisher. The two together produce a beautiful, fragrant oil that provides instant relief for dry skin.

Ingredients
   2 cups sunflower oil
   1 handful dried lavender

Pour sunflower oil into medium-sized mixing bowl. Add lavender. Stir until flowers are well distributed throughout oil. Pour oil into glass or plastic container with airtight lid or cork. Allow to sit two to three weeks. Apply as needed.

Storage and life span: Although this product takes longer to make than most others, it also yields a large batch of fragrant oil that will easily last several months. The longer the herb sits in the oil, the more fragrant and "active" it will become.

ALOE VERA-RASPBERRY GEL

Aloe vera rules supreme when it comes to nursing dry, cracked, sunburned, or weatherbeaten skin. Raspberry heals and invigorates the skin as it helps restore its pH (acid/alkaline) balance. Together these ingredients make a refreshing, summery dry-skin soother. If you're feeling mighty ambitious, you could use the oil from your own aloe plant for this recipe, but for the sake of time and effort, you're better off just picking up some pure aloe vera gel at your drugstore.

Ingredients

1 cup aloe vera gel
2 tablespoons raspberry herbal tea leaves

Combine ingredients in heat-resistant bowl. Bring about two inches of water to boil in saucepan. Place bowl in boiling water (like double boiler). Heat until liquefied and raspberry leaves infuse into gel. Remove from heat and allow to cool. Then strain aromatic gel into lotion dispenser.

Storage and life span: Store in a cool, dark place. Will last as long as any commercial lotion.

VITAMIN E HEALER

Almonds, sunflower seeds, and wheat germ are all excellent sources of vitamin E, which not only helps soothe and heal dry, flaky skin, it also diminishes the appearance of fine lines and wrinkles. This recipe combines the oils of all three for a dry-skin trio that will leave your skin soft, supple, and smooth.

Ingredients
- 1/3 cup sunflower oil
- 1/4 cup almond oil
- 1/8 cup wheat germ oil

Blend three oils together in mixing bowl and transfer to glass or plastic bottle with airtight lid. Gently turn bottle upside down and right side up before each use to keep oils blended. Apply as needed.

Storage and life span: Store in a cool, dark place. Will last as long as any commercial lotion.

FACIAL TONERS

If you're not careful, everyday living can wreak havoc on your skin. Too little sleep, too much stress, too many hectic fast-food meals, and too much exposure to wind, heat, and cold can leave you with a rough, patchy complexion and maybe even bouts of acne. Though facial toners aren't a cure-all for those facial woes, they can help keep your skin looking fresh and clean by removing the top layer of dead skin cells so that the healthy young skin below can be seen. Used regularly, toners can improve the overall look and feel of your skin.

CITRUS-VODKA TONER

Oranges are a rich source of vitamin C, which scientists now know helps to build collagen—the skin's support system—and keeps skin firm and smooth. Lemons are indispensable beauty aids that cleanse oily skin, lightly bleach dark patches and freckles, and remove dirt and grease from pores. Vodka is a natural astringent that helps keep oily skin in check.

Ingredients
    3   cups water
    1   peel from small orange
  1/2   lemon, peel from
    2   tablespoons vodka

Bring water to boil. Place orange and lemon peel in medium-sized heat-resistant bowl. Pour boiling water over citrus peels. Allow to steep until citrus water has cooled and then add vodka. Mix well. Pour mixture into squirt or spray bottle. Apply daily, or as needed, with fresh cotton ball. Shake well before using.

Storage and life span: Store unused mixture in a cool, dark place. Will last for about three weeks.

CUCUMBER-CHAMOMILE COMPLEX

Cucumber may be one of the most healing vegetables when it comes to skin care. It has a pH factor similar to the skin's and restores a healthy balance to our complexions while it cleanses and heals. The fragrant herb chamomile not only makes an excellent tea, it also reduces skin inflammation and helps clear up blocked pores. This mixture makes a superb facial toner.

Ingredients
2 cups water
4 teaspoons chamomile herbal tea (or 3 tea bags)
1/4 cup peeled, cubed cucumber

Bring water to boil. Pour over chamomile tea in heat-resistant canning jar or mixing bowl. Cover and allow to steep for twenty minutes. Uncover and allow mixture to cool. While mixture is cooling, pour cucumber cubes in blender and mix on medium-high until vegetable is liquefied. Strain cucumber blend through paper towel, coffee filter, or cheesecloth, collecting liquid in small mixing bowl. Combine cooled chamomile tea with cucumber liquid; mix well. Transfer liquid into squirt or spray bottle. Apply daily, or as needed, with fresh cotton ball. Shake well before using.

Storage and life span: Cucumber doesn't last very long. Keep stored in the refrigerator and discard after two to three days.

GRAPE JUICE ELIXIR

Grapes, both white and red, contain beautifying acids known as alpha hydroxy acids (AHAs) that gently exfoliate dead skin cells, diminishing the appearance of fine lines and wrinkles. Because this can dry your skin a little, try adding a little oatmeal and a dash of honey. This will help nourish, condition, and soften the tender layer of smooth skin the grape juice uncovers.

Ingredients

- 1/2 cup prepared oatmeal
- 1/2 cup water
- 1 teaspoon honey
- 3/4 cup seedless grapes (red or white)

In blender, mix oatmeal, water, honey, and grapes on medium speed until smooth and pureed. Filter mixture through paper towel, coffee filter, or cheesecloth, collecting filtered mixture in mixing bowl. Transfer liquid to squirt or spray bottle. Apply daily, or as needed, with fresh cotton ball.

Storage and life span: Store unused product in the refrigerator. Discard after four or five days.

COLD CREAMS

There may be no gentler, more beneficial way to remove the day's dirt and makeup from your face than with a skin-soothing cold cream. The product was originally called "cole cream" after its main ingredient, cole seed oil, but the name "cold cream" evolved from centuries of mispronouncing "cole cream." Used daily, cold creams can help fight the signs of aging by toning, moisturizing, and firming delicate facial skin.

MEDITERRANEAN COLD CREAM

Beeswax is an all-natural product secreted by bees to form their combs. It's a must-have ingredient in almost all homemade cold creams because it forms a protective layer on the surface of the skin while it locks in moisture. Almond oil is excellent for combating dry skin and keeping facial skin soft and smooth. The best time to use this fragrant mixture is right before bedtime.

Ingredients
- 1/2 cup almond oil (may substitute with olive oil)
- 2 tablespoons grated beeswax (available at health-food stores)
- 5 tablespoons springwater
- 1/4 teaspoon borax powder

Combine oil and beeswax in heat-resistant glass measuring cup or mixing bowl. Fill saucepan with about two inches of water and bring to boil. Place cup or bowl in saucepan (like double boiler) and heat oil-beeswax mixture, stirring occasionally, until beeswax is melted. In another saucepan, bring springwater to boil and add borax powder, stirring until completely dissolved. Remove oil-beeswax mixture from stove and slowly add borax-water while beating mixture vigorously with whisk. Pour creamy mixture into small container with airtight lid. Allow to cool before using.

Storage and life span: Store in a cool, dark place. Will last eight months to a year.

TROPICAL-BLEND COLD CREAM

Coconut oil is a thick, rich conditioner that will leave your skin soft and smelling of the fragrant tropics. Beeswax forms a protective layer on the surface of the skin, shielding it from pollutants and irritants while locking in moisture. Together, these ingredients yield a luxurious cold cream that will help keep your complexion at its softest, most supple best.

Ingredients
- 1/2 cup coconut oil
- 1 1/2 tablespoons grated beeswax (available at health-food stores)
- 5 tablespoons springwater
- 1/8 teaspoon borax powder
- 1/2 teaspoon almond extract

Combine oil and beeswax in heat-resistant glass measuring cup or mixing bowl. Fill saucepan with about two inches of water and bring to boil. Place cup or bowl in saucepan (like double boiler) and heat oil-beeswax mixture, stirring occasionally, until beeswax is melted. In another saucepan, bring springwater to boil and add borax powder, stirring until completely dissolved. Remove oil-beeswax mixture from stove and slowly add borax-water while beating mixture vigorously with whisk. Add almond extract. Mix well. Pour creamy mixture into small container with airtight lid. Allow to cool before using.

Storage and life span: Store in a cool, dark place. Will last eight months to a year.

LUSCIOUS LIP BALMS

Next to your eyes, nothing on your face is as expressive as your lips. You smile with them, laugh with them, and, of course, kiss with them! Naturally, you always want them to be as soft and supple as possible. But daily wear and tear can take their toll on your tender lip skin, leaving it chapped and dry. These recipes will help protect your lips from the elements and at the same time lock in their moisturizing agents. You can wear lip balms by themselves or on top of your regular lipstick.

COCOA-COCOA LIP PROTECTION

As folks in the sun-scorched tropics will tell you, there is probably no better emollient than cocoa butter. Thick and rich, cocoa butter conditions and moisturizes, leaving behind a smooth, silky—and kissable!—finish. A dash of cocoa powder adds a mildly sweet taste and just a touch of color to this luscious lip balm.

Ingredients
1 teaspoon grated cocoa butter
1/2 teaspoon grated beeswax
1 teaspoon sunflower oil
1/4 teaspoon sweetened or semisweetened cocoa powder

Combine all ingredients in heat-resistant glass measuring cup or mixing bowl. Fill small saucepan with about two inches of water and bring to boil. Place cup or bowl in saucepan (like double boiler) and allow ingredients to melt, stirring occasionally.

When beeswax and butter are completely melted, remove from heat and stir until thoroughly blended. Pour mixture into lip-balm container (small round tub with screw-on top works best). Allow to cool before using.

Storage and life span: Store in a cool place to prevent remelting. Will last up to a year.

LICORICE LIP GLOSS

This lip gloss actually gets its fragrant licorice-candy flavor from anise extract. Anise is a wonderfully medicinal herb that can help soothe general skin irritations, such as dry, chapped lips. A touch of almond oil makes this tasty lip balm even more soothing for sore lips.

Ingredients
   1   tablespoon grated beeswax
   1/2   tablespoon almond oil
   2   drops anise extract

Combine beeswax and almond oil in heat-resistant glass measuring cup or mixing bowl. Fill small saucepan with about two inches of water and bring to boil. Place cup or bowl in saucepan (like double boiler) and allow ingredients to melt, stirring occasionally. When beeswax is completely melted, remove mixture from heat, add anise extract, and stir until thoroughly blended. Pour mixture into lip-balm container (small round tub with screw-on top works best). Allow to cool before using.

Storage and life span: Store in a cool place to prevent remelting. Will last up to a year.

ALOE-E LIP RELIEF

This is the perfect recipe for parched summer lips. Aloe vera gel provides cool, healing relief, while the vitamin E nourishes and moisturizes. You can use this mixture as a gel, or if you prefer a longer-lasting shine, you can add a little petroleum jelly to give it more staying power.

Ingredients

1   tablespoon aloe vera gel
3   drops vitamin E oil (can take from vitamin E capsule)
2   teaspoons petroleum jelly (optional)

Combine ingredients in heat-resistant glass measuring cup or mixing bowl. Fill small saucepan with about two inches of water and bring to boil. Place cup or bowl in saucepan (like double boiler) and allow ingredients to melt, stirring occasionally. When mixture is well blended, remove from heat. Pour mixture into lip-balm container (small round tub with screw-on top works best). Allow to cool before using.

Storage and life span: Store in a cool place to prevent remelting. Will last up to a year.

EYE AND NECK CREAMS

As you likely already know, the thin, delicate skin around your eyes and neck is the first place you start to show fine lines, wrinkles, and other signs of age. You can help keep this sensitive skin smooth and supple with the right products, but commercial eye and neck creams can cost a great deal. Fortunately, you can make your own creams with basic ingredients you may already have around the house.

OLIVE-COCOA BUTTER NECK CREAM

Cocoa butter is a longtime favorite among women around the world for keeping the delicate neck skin smooth and firm. It also leaves a silky protective finish that locks in moisture and keeps skin soft to the touch. Olive oil is another old-time favorite for conditioning and softening the skin. Together, these rich emollients make a smooth, fragrant cream that will keep your neck supple for years to come.

Ingredients
- 3 tablespoons grated cocoa butter
- 1/2 cup olive oil
- 1 teaspoon petroleum jelly

Combine ingredients in heat-resistant glass measuring cup or mixing bowl. Fill small saucepan with about two inches of water and bring to boil. Place cup or bowl in saucepan (like double boiler) and allow ingredients to melt, stirring occasionally. When ingredients have completely melted, remove mixture from heat and stir until thoroughly blended. Pour mixture into sterile cold-cream container (the kind with screw-on cap works best). Allow to cool before using.

Storage and life span: Store in a cool place to prevent remelting. Will last about four months.

COCONUT CREAM EYES

Coconut oil is a thick, saturated fat that is made by pressing coconut flesh. It makes a delightfully rich skin moisturizer and conditioner, which is why it's such a popular ingredient in suntan oils and lotions. And it smells delicious! This recipe also includes a dab of petroleum jelly to help keep all that moisture locked in.

Ingredients
3 tablespoons grated beeswax
1/2 cup coconut oil
1 teaspoon petroleum jelly

Combine ingredients in heat-resistant glass measuring cup or mixing bowl. Fill small saucepan with about two inches of water and bring to boil. Place cup or bowl in saucepan (like double boiler) and allow ingredients to melt, stirring occasionally. When ingredients are completely melted, remove mixture from heat and stir until thoroughly blended. Pour mixture into sterile cold-cream container (the kind with screw-on cap works best). Allow to cool before using.

Storage and life span: Store in a cool place to prevent remelting. Will last about ten to twelve weeks.

CHAMOMILE TEA TONER

A popular herb among European women, chamomile is a soothing skin healer that not only reduces skin inflammation—like the puffiness around your eyes—it also helps cleanse pores. Sunflower oil is brimming with skin-healing vitamin E and makes a wonderful skin conditioner and moisturizer. Lavender helps stimulate circulation. Together, these healthful ingredients will keep the delicate skin around your eyes and neck nourished and supple.

Ingredients

- 1/2 cup water
- 4 chamomile tea bags
- 1/2 cup sunflower oil
- 2 drops lavender essential oil (optional)

Bring water to boil. Remove from heat and add tea bags. Allow to steep for fifteen to twenty minutes. Add sunflower oil and lavender oil, if using. Mix well with whisk. Pour product into sterilized salad-dressing bottle or other sterile squirt-top container. Shake well before using. Apply around eye area with fingertips. As with any cosmetic product, avoid getting mixture in eyes.

Storage and life span: Store in a cool, dark, and dry place. Can last up to ten to twelve weeks.

SKIN BRACERS AND AFTERSHAVES

We don't have to tell you about the havoc shaving can wreak on your skin. All that pulling and scraping, the ingrown hairs, the razor burn. Whether you're a woman shaving her legs or a man shaving his face, it can be pretty rough going. That's why skin bracers and aftershaves were invented. They not only give your skin an attractive smell, they help seal the microscopic cuts and nicks caused by shaving, leaving you less prone to inflammation afterward.

OLD-TIME HAZEL AND SAGE

Witch hazel may be the best all-around natural remedy for minor burns, cuts, scratches, itches, and abrasions of all kinds. Its astringent action makes it a perfect aftershave because it disinfects skin and closes pores. Sage is another ancient facial remedy, particularly for cleansing and toning skin. These two ingredients combined make a pleasantly aromatic, refreshing aftershave.

Ingredients
3/4 cup witch hazel
2 tablespoons dried sage

Combine ingredients in clean container with tight-fitting lid. Leave in cool, dark place for ten days. Filter sage from liquid and transfer product to aftershave bottle.

Storage and life span: Store in a cool, dark place. Will last for six to eight months.

Pirate's Rum Skin Bracer

Maybe the pirates originally used this spicy spirit for skin care and only later discovered that it made a pretty potent drink as well. Or maybe it was the other way around. In any case, rum is an excellent oil remover and facial toner. A splash of essential rosemary oil makes the mixture a nice conditioner, too.

Ingredients

- 1/4 cup rum
- 1/4 cup springwater
- 1/8 cup witch hazel
- 2–3 drops rosemary essential oil (optional)

Combine all ingredients in aftershave bottle. Shake before using.

Storage and life span: Store in a cool, dark place. Will last for six to eight months.

VODKA SPLASH

Like its sister spirit rum, vodka makes a superb facial cleanser and toner. It's also quite astringent, which makes it perfect for "bracing" skin after a shave. The apple cider vinegar added to this recipe helps to alleviate the dry flakiness that often accompanies frequent shaving.

Ingredients

- 1/4 cup vodka
- 1/4 cup apple cider vinegar
- 1/4 cup springwater

Combine all ingredients in aftershave bottle. Shake before using.

Storage and life span: Store in a cool, dark place. Will last for six to eight months.

HIS AND HER AFTERSHAVE

Personal-care products suitable for either men or women are
increasingly popular. This crisp, refreshing aftershave uses
witch hazel, which disinfects skin and closes pores, as a base.
And it contains just a hint of lavender, which gives it a light
and pleasant aroma.

Ingredients

$1/2$ cup witch hazel
1 teaspoon dried lavender (or 2 drops lavender essential oil)

If you're using lavender oil, just combine ingredients and use
right away. If you use leaves, mix ingredients in clean container
with tight lid and leave in cool, dark place for ten days. Strain
out lavender leaves. Transfer liquid to aftershave bottle and use
as needed.

Storage and life span: Store in a cool, dark place. Will last for
six to eight months.

Chapter 4

Healthy Hair

Dating back to Samson and Delilah—and maybe even to cave women curling their hair around dinosaur bones—we have been preoccupied with our hair. We spend hours combing, crimping, and styling it. How good or bad our hair looks has a definite effect on our moods. Who hasn't been sent into a funk by a bad hair day? And, contrary to popular belief, being well-coiffed is as important to men as it is to women. It's little wonder, then, that we're willing to drop hundreds of dollars a year on an endless stream of hair-care products, including shampoos, conditioners, gels, color enhancers, lighteners, and cover-ups, to name just a few!

That's the bad news. The good news is that we don't have to spend a fortune to achieve beautiful hair. Natural ingredients such as eggs, vinegar, and beer can do a better job of cleaning and nourishing hair than chemical and alcohol-laden shampoos can—and for a fraction of the cost. In this section you'll find shampoo recipes for all hair types, as well as recipes for conditioners, highlighters, gray cover-ups, and color enhancers. Once you become familiar with the ingredients, you can experiment and make your very own products. But remember: your hair, like your skin, depends on good nutrition, proper rest, and a wholesome lifestyle to be at its healthiest, shiniest best.

BASIC BEAUTY SHAMPOOS

Though hair technically is considered dead, it is really quite alive. It's an extension of the outer layer of your skin known as the epidermis. Your hair grows as the hair follicles absorb nutrients and amino acids from the blood flow that nourishes your scalp. After these cells push upward, they die, forming a hard protein called keratin. Eventually, old hair is shed, and new strands grow in. But after age thirty the cycle between growing new hair and shedding old begins to slow. And since you have more older hair on your head, it is especially important to take care of it. The following basic beauty shampoos can help. Note: These recipes produce a shampoo that feels thinner than commercial shampoos but that works just as well. For a thicker shampoo, just add more soap.

SWEET PARSLEY SHAMPOO

Rich in vitamins A and C, parsley is a healer, cleanser, and soother. It's the perfect ingredient for keeping the delicate skin on your scalp nourished and healthy. The touch of safflower oil in this shampoo makes an excellent conditioner and also helps to lock in moisture to prevent hair from drying out and breaking. Use as you would any commercial shampoo.

Ingredients
- 3/4 cup water
- 1 handful fresh parsley (or 2 teaspoons dried parsley)
- 8 tablespoons pure soap flakes
  (or 1/2 cup liquid soap for sensitive skin)
- 1/2 teaspoon safflower oil

Bring water to boil. Remove from stove and pour into mixing bowl. Add parsley. Allow to sit for ten to fifteen minutes. Strain

into another mixing bowl. Add soap flakes and safflower oil.
Mix well. Allow to sit until mixture thickens. Pour into clean
plastic bottle, such as shampoo or conditioner bottle.

Storage and life span: Store in a cool, dark place. Will last for
twelve to sixteen weeks.

CHAMOMILE-LAVENDER SHAMPOO

The fragrant chamomile flower does a wonderful job of opening
pores, refreshing skin and hair, soothing and healing skin, and
improving circulation. In other words, it has all the makings of
an ideal shampoo. In addition, these bright, beautiful flowers
give light brown and blonde hair a burst of gentle highlights.
The precious oils found in lavender flowers are top-notch hair
conditioners. Combined, these two make a great shampoo that
will leave your hair soft and healthy. Add a touch of safflower
oil for extra conditioning power.

Ingredients

- 3/4 cup water
- 1 handful fresh or dried chamomile flowers
- 2 tablespoons dried lavender flowers
- 8 tablespoons pure soap flakes
  (or 1/2 cup liquid soap for sensitive skin)
- 1/2 teaspoon safflower oil (optional)

Bring water to boil and then pour into mixing bowl. Add
chamomile and lavender. Allow to sit for ten to fifteen minutes.
Strain into another mixing bowl. Add soap flakes and safflower
oil, if using. Mix well. Allow to sit until mixture thickens. Pour
into clean plastic bottle, such as shampoo or conditioner bottle.

Storage and life span: Store in a cool, dark place. Will last for twelve to sixteen weeks.

"Spirited" Shampoo

Made from hops, barley, yeast, and water, beer is the perfect way to give your hair volume, adding bounce and life to all hair types but particularly to thin, flyaway hair. When using beer in shampoos, make sure the beer is flat or else the alcohol will have a drying effect. (For best results, open a canor bottle and let it sit for two days.) Eggs also add volume to hair. The vitamin- and mineral-rich yolk is especially good for nourishing dry hair.

Ingredients

3/4 cup water
8 tablespoons pure soap flakes
   (or 1/2 cup liquid soap for sensitive skin)
1/3 cup stale beer
1 raw egg
1/2 teaspoon olive oil

Bring water to boil. Remove from stove and pour into mixing bowl. Add soap flakes. Mix well. Warm beer in saucepan on stove until it begins to simmer. Remove from heat and add to soap flake-water mixture. Stir well. Let sit until completely cool, then add egg and olive oil and mix well. Pour into clean plastic bottle, such as shampoo or conditioner bottle. This shampoo works best when used with cool water. Be sure to rinse hair thoroughly after shampooing. Mix well before each use.

Storage and life span: Raw eggs are highly perishable. Store in the refrigerator. Will last for one to two weeks.

THE CAT'S MEOW SHAMPOO

Catnip is traditionally believed to promote hair growth. While no one can say for certain whether there's any validity to that bit of folklore, catnip does add a fresh scent to this basic cleansing shampoo. The sunflower oil adds a nice touch of nourishing vitamin E and helps condition hair.

Ingredients

- 3/4 cup water
- 1 handful fresh catnip (or 2 teaspoons dried herb)
- 8 tablespoons pure soap flakes
  (or 1/2 cup liquid soap for sensitive skin)
- 1/2 teaspoon sunflower oil

Bring water to boil. Remove from stove and pour into mixing bowl. Add catnip. Allow to sit for ten to fifteen minutes. Strain into another mixing bowl. Add soap flakes and sunflower oil. Mix well. Allow to sit until mixture thickens. Pour into clean plastic bottle, such as shampoo or conditioner bottle.

Storage and life span: Store in a cool, dark place. Will last for twelve to sixteen weeks.

FOR OILY HAIR ONLY

Oily hair, as anyone who has it will attest, may be the most difficult to keep in line. You wash it in the morning and by the afternoon it needs to be washed again. Because of the highly productive oil glands in their scalps, people with oily hair need a shampoo that will accomplish two things: remove excess oil from hair shafts and leave the scalp toned and squeaky clean. Following are some natural products that can help. Note: These recipes produce a shampoo that feels thinner than commercial shampoos but that works just as well. For a thicker feel, just add more soap.

Sage Shampoo

Sage is a wonderfully aromatic astringent for oily hair. It not only lifts oil from the hair follicles, it also tightens the pores of the scalp, helping to stem the flow of oil from the skin to the hair. As a bonus, sage helps cleanse the scalp of dandruff. Folklore praises sage as a panacea of sorts: good for strengthening the mind as well as the muscles. While it probably doesn't do that, it is good for your hair.

Ingredients
- 3/4 cup water
- 2 tablespoons dried sage
- 8 tablespoons pure soap flakes
  (or 1/2 cup liquid soap for sensitive skin)

Bring water to boil. Remove from stove and pour into mixing bowl. Add sage. Allow to sit for ten to fifteen minutes. Strain into another mixing bowl. Add soap flakes. Mix well. Allow to sit until mixture thickens. Pour into clean plastic bottle, such as shampoo or conditioner bottle.

Storage and life span: Store in a cool, dark place. Will last for twelve to sixteen weeks.

LEMON-RUM SHAMPOO

Rum is both a fine tropical drink and a superb tonic for oily hair. Amber or white, rum lifts dirt and oil from the hair and scalp, leaving them feeling and smelling clean. Lemon cuts through built-up dirt and grime. Together, these two potent ingredients leave even the oiliest of hair clean, fresh, and healthy.

Ingredients
- $3/4$ cup water
- $1/2$ lemon rind, coarsely grated
- 10 tablespoons pure soap flakes
  (or $2/3$ cup liquid soap for sensitive skin)
- $1/8$ cup white or amber rum

Bring water to boil. Remove from stove and pour into mixing bowl. Add lemon rind. Allow to sit for ten to fifteen minutes. Strain into another mixing bowl. Add soap flakes and rum. Mix well. Allow to sit until mixture thickens. Pour into clean plastic bottle, such as shampoo or conditioner bottle. Shake well before using.

Storage and life span: Store in a cool, dark place. Will last for twelve to sixteen weeks.

WHITE VINEGAR HAIR CLEANSER

Vinegar is a classic cosmetic ingredient for skin and hair care. It's an excellent cleanser, it removes excess oil, it helps create a normal pH (acid/alkaline) balance to your skin, it smooths flaky skin, and it provides dandruff relief. Some people believe that vinegar is useful for restoring your body's energy when you're feeling fatigued. So use it generously!

Ingredients
- 1/4 cup water
- 1/4 cup white vinegar
- 1/2 cup mild liquid soap (or baby shampoo)

Blend all ingredients in small saucepan. Heat on medium on stove top until mixture becomes warm. Use whisk to stir ingredients until thoroughly blended. Pour into clean plastic bottle, such as shampoo or conditioner bottle.

Storage and life span: Store in a cool, dark place. Will last for twelve to sixteen weeks. Shake before using if product has separated.

LEMONGRASS-THYME EXTRA PROTECTION

Often used to season Asian soups, lemongrass also is a fragrant, refreshing astringent, great for transforming oily hair into squeaky clean hair. Lemongrass helps tone the skin of the scalp, tightening pores so that skin and hair feel less oily longer. Thyme acts as a toning astringent and gentle antiseptic that will help keep your scalp healthy. Together, these two powerful herbs produce super protection from oily hair.

Ingredients

  1 cup water
  1 tablespoon dried lemongrass
  1 tablespoon dried thyme
 10 tablespoons pure soap flakes
    (or about $2/3$ cup liquid soap for sensitive skin)

Bring water to boil. Remove from stove and pour into mixing bowl. Add lemongrass and thyme. Allow to sit for ten to fifteen minutes. Strain into another mixing bowl. Add soap flakes. Mix well. Allow to sit until mixture thickens. Pour into clean plastic bottle, such as shampoo or conditioner bottle.

Storage and life span: Store in a cool, dark place. Will last for twelve to sixteen weeks.

DRY-HAIR REVIVERS

As we age, our glands naturally begin to secrete less oil, leaving our skin, scalp, and consequently our hair drier than it was when we were younger. Of course, all the perming, coloring, and processing our hair endures also strips away oil. For people with oily hair, this drying effect can be a welcome relief. But for folks with normal or dry hair, the loss of their natural oils leaves hair increasingly dry, brittle, and susceptible to damage. Dry hair also has less life and luster than hair shining with natural oils. The simple solution for a parched mane is to use shampoos and treatments that add a protective layer of oil to your scalp and hair shaft.

HONEY OF A SHAMPOO

Made by bees from the nectar of flowers, golden honey is an excellent moisturizer and humectant (moisture trapper). Honey also leaves a shiny, silky finish on skin and hair. The sunflower oil in this recipe adds a touch of nourishing vitamin E, which will give your hair a well-conditioned luster. Together, these ingredients make a great dry-hair reviver you can use every day.

Ingredients

3/4 cup water
1 tablespoon honey
1/2 teaspoon sunflower oil
8 tablespoons pure soap flakes
(or 1/2 cup liquid soap for sensitive skin)

Blend all ingredients in small saucepan. Heat on medium on stove top until mixture becomes warm. Use whisk to stir ingredients until thoroughly blended. Pour into clean plastic bottle, such as shampoo or conditioner bottle.

Storage and life span: Store in a cool, dark place. Will last for eight to twelve weeks. Shake before using if product separates.

ALOHA ALOE REMEDY

Thick, rich, and deliciously fragrant, coconut oil is one of the richest emollients on the planet. It moisturizes dry, brittle hair, leaving behind a smooth protective film that will keep your locks looking their best. Aloe vera, well-known for its ability to alleviate sun-scorched dry skin, also provides needed relief for parched hair shafts. This rich, tropical-smelling shampoo will leave you with a full, luxurious head of hair.

Ingredients
- 1/2 cup water
- 3 tablespoons aloe vera gel
- 1/2 teaspoon coconut oil
- 1/2 cup mild liquid soap (or baby shampoo)

Blend all ingredients in small saucepan. Heat on medium on stove top until mixture becomes warm. Use whisk to stir ingredients until thoroughly blended. Pour into clean plastic bottle, such as shampoo or conditioner bottle.

Storage and life span: Store in a cool, dark place. Will last for twelve to sixteen weeks. Shake before using if product has separated.

Mediterranean Radiance

This recipe works best for dry, brittle, or heavily processed hair. Egg yolks are rich in fatty acids and essential vitamins that enrich your scalp and hair. Likewise, olive oil is brimming with essential fats and vitamin E, a skin and hair nourisher. As the beautiful, dark-haired women of the Mediterranean have known for years, olive oil will leave your tresses smooth and lustrous, as will this shampoo. Because it's so rich, this recipe should be used no more than once or twice a week.

Ingredients
    1   cup water
   10   tablespoons pure soap flakes
        (or $2/3$ cup liquid soap for sensitive skin)
    3   tablespoons olive oil
    2   egg yolks

Bring water to boil. Remove from stove and pour water into mixing bowl. Add soap flakes. Mix well. Add oil to soap flake-water mixture. Stir well. Let sit until completely cool, then add egg yolks and mix well. Pour into clean plastic bottle, such as shampoo or conditioner bottle. This shampoo works best when used with cool water. Be sure to rinse hair thoroughly after shampooing.

Storage and life span: Since raw eggs are highly perishable, this product must be stored in the refrigerator. Will last for one to two weeks. Be sure to mix thoroughly before each use.

HOT-OIL THERAPY

All five oils in this super-nourishing hot-oil treatment have one thing in common: they're all rich with skin- and hair-enriching vitamin E. These oils will moisturize your hair and give it a silky, smooth finish. They'll also tone the skin on your scalp to help keep your hair naturally shiny for days. You can use this treatment once a week if your hair is very dry. Use it less frequently for normal to dry hair.

Ingredients

- 1 tablespoon olive oil
- 1 tablespoon sunflower oil
- 1 tablespoon peanut oil
- 1 tablespoon almond oil
- 1 tablespoon safflower oil

In saucepan, combine all oils over low heat. Stir ingredients until they begin to warm up and give off steam. When warm, remove from heat. Allow to cool slightly. Then massage treatment into hair and allow to sit for ten to fifteen minutes. Rinse and shampoo as usual.

Storage and life span: It's best to make a fresh batch before each application. If you find yourself with too much left over, simply reduce the amount of each oil.

DANDRUFF TREATMENTS

We all recognize the symptoms of dandruff: unsightly white flakes on our clothes and an incessantly itchy scalp. It can be pretty hard to find the solution to this problem, especially if you spend much of your time in dry, indoor conditions or live in a cold, dry climate. Some commercial dandruff shampoos can help fight this problem, but not without a significant price tag. And many of them have a strong odor that is anything but clean-smelling. The better solution to your dandruff problem is to take matters into your own hands by using natural, homemade products. Here are a few that can have your scalp flake-free in no time.

TOTAL HEAD REMEDY

Salicylic acid, found in aspirin, is an important active ingredient in many commercial dandruff shampoos. It tones the scalp, exfoliates dandruff, and helps prevent flakes from recurring. The lemon rind in this recipe not only gives your skin and hair a fresh, clean smell, it also acts as a hair and scalp exfoliater and softener. This shampoo is gentle enough to use every day.

Ingredients
  1 cup water
 1/2 rind of lemon
 10 tablespoons pure soap flakes
      (or 2/3 cup liquid soap for sensitive skin)
  2 aspirin tablets, crushed
 1/4 teaspoon olive oil

Bring water to boil. Remove from stove and pour into mixing bowl. Add lemon rind. Allow to sit for ten to fifteen minutes. Strain into another mixing bowl. Add soap flakes, crushed aspirin, and olive oil. Mix well. Allow to sit until mixture thickens. Pour into clean plastic bottle, such as shampoo or conditioner bottle.

Storage and life span: Store in a cool, dark place. Will last for twelve to sixteen weeks.

APPLE-VINEGAR DANDRUFF CONTROL

Vinegar is a staple of many homemade beauty products, and hair-care products are no exception. This potent, fermented solution helps restore your skin's natural pH (acid/alkaline) balance, and it strips away existing flakes and softens dry, flaky skin. The dash of aloe vera neutralizes the distinct vinegary smell of this shampoo and adds skin-softening power all its own.

Ingredients

1/4 cup apple cider vinegar
2 tablespoons aloe vera gel
1 tablespoon olive oil
3/4 cup warm water

Pour ingredients into blender. Blend together on medium-low speed for about thirty seconds. Pour into clean plastic bottle, such as shampoo or conditioner bottle. Massage into scalp and allow to work for about five minutes. Rinse well with warm water. This shampoo works even better if you keep a little apple cider vinegar on hand to spritz onto hair while you rinse.

Storage and life span: Store in a cool, dark place. Will last for four to six weeks. Shake well before using.

ROSEMARY-THYME FLAKE CONTROL

Rosemary was once thought to stimulate hair follicles to help promote hair growth. While we know today that this fragrant herb won't grow hair, it does help tone the skin on the scalp to prevent dandruff. Thyme, another aromatic herb long used to fight eczema, helps to tone skin and to relieve dry, itchy dandruff. A dash of almond oil helps keep skin and hair soft and conditioned. Together, these ingredients make a wonderfully fragrant medicinal shampoo.

Ingredients
$3/4$ cup water
1 tablespoon dried rosemary
1 tablespoon dried thyme
8 tablespoons pure soap flakes
   (or $1/2$ cup liquid soap for sensitive skin)
$1/2$ teaspoon almond oil

Bring water to boil. Remove from stove and pour into mixing bowl. Add rosemary and thyme. Allow to sit for ten to fifteen minutes. Strain into another mixing bowl. Add soap flakes and almond oil. Mix well. Allow to sit until mixture thickens. Pour into clean plastic bottle, such as shampoo or conditioner bottle.

Storage and life span: Store in a cool, dark place. Will last for twelve to sixteen weeks.

DETANGLERS AND CONDITIONERS

Anyone who's ever endured the yanking and pulling of a mother's relentless comb through tangled young locks understands the merciful benefit of detanglers and conditioners. Hair can become hopelessly knotted during shampooing and drying unless we add a smoothing agent to slightly coat the hair shaft. While you can buy commercial conditioners to help keep your hair soft, shiny, and tangle-free, there are plenty of ingredients right in your own pantry that work just as well without the high cost or the chemical buildup.

CREAMY AVOCADO CONDITIONER

The buttery flesh of the avocado is rich with essential fatty acids that nourish your scalp and leave a light protective coating on your hair. As a bonus, it smells absolutely delicious! The eggs in this recipe provide valuable proteins that help condition and revive dry, damaged hair. A dash of olive oil adds a touch of skin- and hair-enriching vitamin E, as well as a little natural oil for a healthy sheen.

Ingredients
- $1/2$ mashed avocado
- 2 eggs
- 1 teaspoon olive oil
- $1/4$ cup water

Put all ingredients in blender. Mix on low speed for about twenty seconds, or until avocado lumps are worked out and mixture is smooth. Avoid blending at high speed or eggs will become overly frothy. Pour into clean shampoo or conditioner bottle. Apply to hair after shampooing. Allow to work for at least three minutes. Rinse well with warm water.

Storage and life span: Keep refrigerated when not in use. Discard after five days.

Honey-Almond Hair Treatment

Rich and smooth, honey is nature's conditioner and humectant (moisture trapper). This sweet creation of bees also heals skin and keeps the scalp nourished and problem-free. Almond oil is rich in vitamin E, which also nourishes skin and hair. A splash of lemon juice adds a refreshing zing and helps exfoliate dead skin.

Ingredients
- $1/4$ cup honey
- 3 tablespoons almond oil
- $1/2$ teaspoon lemon juice

Pour ingredients into small saucepan. Heat on medium low, stirring gently with whisk. Continue warming and stirring until mixture is thoroughly blended. Remove from heat and pour into clean shampoo or conditioner bottle. Work small amount through damp hair. Allow to sit for about five minutes. Shampoo as usual and rinse well with warm water.

Storage and life span: Store in a cool, dark place. Will last eight to twelve weeks. Product may separate when not in use. If it does, simply run the bottle under warm to hot water and shake well before using.

FRUIT 'N' HONEY CONDITIONER

Chock-full of potassium and vitamin C, bananas can make a fragrant skin and hair conditioner. Cantaloupe, also rich in essential nutrients, including vitamin C and B-complex vitamins, is one of the best fruits for maintaining healthy, shiny hair. Both are low in acid, so they're easy on sensitive skin.

Ingredients

- 1/2 banana, sliced
- 1/2 cantaloupe, chopped
- 1 tablespoon honey

Put fruit and honey in blender. Blend on low speed for ten to fifteen seconds, or until mixture reaches smooth and fluid but not overly watery consistency. Pour into clean shampoo or conditioner bottle. Apply to hair immediately after shampooing. Leave on for five minutes. Rinse well with lukewarm water.

Storage and life span: These fresh ingredients turn bad rather quickly, so it's best to make fresh batches frequently. Unused portion can be stored in the refrigerator for two to three days.

YOGURT-MAYO SOFTENER

Yogurt is a mild skin exfoliater and cleanser. Because it's rich in proteins, it leaves a silky finish on skin and hair. Mayonnaise, which contains eggs, oil, and apple cider vinegar, also is a wonderful skin and hair conditioner. You can use this simple mixture in place of your regular deep-conditioning treatment.

Ingredients
1/2 cup mayonnaise
1/2 cup plain yogurt

Combine ingredients in medium-sized mixing bowl and blend well, using whisk. Spoon into cold-cream tub. Massage into damp hair. Allow to work for ten to fifteen minutes. Shampoo and condition as usual. Use about once every week for very dry or damaged hair.

Storage and life span: Keep refrigerated. Will last for five to seven days.

BUILDUP REMOVERS

We love our hair sprays, gels, and mousses for the styling control they give us. But using these products day after day and week after week can leave behind a layer of residue that makes our hair feel less clean and look quite dull. Even using the same shampoo over and over can have the same effect. That's why it's important to break your routine every couple of weeks and use a cleansing shampoo specifically designed to wash away residue and buildup. These commercial products can cost twice as much as regular shampoos you buy in a drugstore. So why not make your own simply and inexpensively at home?

TWO-SHOT CLARIFIER

Vodka's effects on hair are profound. As a clear, potent astringent, it strips away excess oil and product buildup, leaving your hair squeaky clean. Likewise, rum is a wonderful shampoo ingredient for removing oil from the scalp and hair follicles and for cutting through buildup to reveal healthy, vibrant hair. The egg added to this recipe helps to clean the hair and adds a bit of conditioning action so that hair isn't left too dry by these highly effective astringents.

Ingredients
- 3 tablespoons vodka
- 3 tablespoons rum
- 1 egg
- 1/2 cup warm water

Place all ingredients in blender. Blend on low speed for fifteen to twenty seconds, or until liquid is smooth and lightly frothy. Pour mixture into clean shampoo or conditioner bottle. Use in place of regular shampoo. Condition as usual.

Storage and life span: Raw eggs do not store well. Keep mixture sealed and refrigerated when not in use. Discard after five days.

Apple Delight Cleanser

While an apple a day may keep the doctor away, a little juice from this healthful fruit may keep unwanted hair buildup away as well. Apple juice is a delightfully light, fragrant astringent that lifts and removes excess oils from hair. Apple cider vinegar helps control dandruff and tones the skin on the scalp. It also helps remove excess dirt and oil. Mix these with a little baby shampoo for a sweet clarifier.

Ingredients
- 1/4 cup apple juice
- 3 tablespoons apple cider vinegar
- 2/3 cup generic baby shampoo

Pour ingredients into small saucepan. Heat on medium low, stirring constantly until ingredients form smooth blend. Remove from heat and transfer to clean shampoo or conditioning bottle. Use in place of your regular shampoo whenever you need to revive dull hair.

Storage and life span: Keep refrigerated when not in use. Will last about two weeks.

HAIR LIGHTENERS AND COLOR ENHANCERS

Whether you love the natural color of your hair, or you actually long for a deeper shade of brown or a lighter shade of blonde, hair lighteners and color enhancers are fun and easy ways to experiment with different hues for your hair. Although commercial hair colors and bleaches can be hard on your hair, expensive, and cumbersome to apply, you can make hair-color enhancers at home that are inexpensive, simple to use, and actually good for your hair.

SIMPLE LEMON LIGHTENER

Packed with vitamin C, the astringent juice of the lemon may be the oldest hair lightener known to man. Spritzing lemon-infused water onto dark blonde hair will bring out naturally bright blonde highlights, especially if you then spend some time out in the sun. It also can bring out highlights and bring up the color of darker hair shades. Remember, though, that undiluted lemon juice is a fairly strong bleach and should never be used straight.

Ingredients

1   cup water
3   drops extra virgin olive oil
1   sliced lemon, rind included

Bring water and oil to boil. Add lemon. Turn down heat and simmer, covered, for ten minutes. Strain mixture and transfer to pump-spray bottle or plastic plant spritzer. Apply to freshly cleaned, damp hair. If possible, sit with hair in sun for fifteen to twenty minutes. Otherwise, dry as usual. Without sun exposure, it will take repeated applications to notice lemon's bleaching effect.

Storage and life span: Keep refrigerated. Will last for seven to ten days.

CHAMOMILE-MULLEIN NATURAL BLONDE

The rich chamomile flower brings its beautiful golden color to hair when used as a lightening rinse on naturally blonde locks. Sweet, fragrant mullein flowers also produce a lovely blonding effect on light-colored hair. Together, these two flowers make a wonderful-smelling rinse that will leave your hair sparkling with highlights.

Ingredients

2 cups water
1/2 teaspoon sunflower oil
1 handful dried chamomile flowers
1 handful dried mullein (or marigold) flowers

Bring water and sunflower oil to boil. Add chamomile and mullein. Lower heat and allow to simmer, covered, for twenty minutes. Strain and transfer to pump-spray bottle or plastic plant spritzer. Apply to freshly cleaned, damp hair. If possible, sit with hair in sun for fifteen to twenty minutes. Otherwise, dry as usual. Without sun exposure, it will take repeated applications to notice flowers' bleaching effect.

Storage and life span: Keep refrigerated. Will last seven to ten days.

ROSEMARY BROWN

The aromatic rosemary herb conditions as well as darkens hair, making it the perfect rinse for brunettes who want to add a little zing to their rich brown hair. The apple cider vinegar in this recipe helps add extra shine.

Ingredients

1 1/2 cups water
  2 tablespoons dried rosemary leaves
  1 teaspoon apple cider vinegar

Bring water to boil. Add rosemary and vinegar. Lower heat and allow to simmer, covered, for twenty minutes. Strain and transfer to pump-spray bottle or plastic plant spritzer. Apply to freshly cleaned, damp hair. Leave on hair for twenty minutes. Rinse well and dry as usual.

Storage and life span: Keep refrigerated. Will last for seven to ten days.

CRANBERRY RED

Rich, red cranberry juice adds a scarlet kick to naturally red hair. The lemon in this recipe lightly bleaches hair to allow the really red highlights to shine through in all their fiery glory. Like most brightening agents, this recipe works best when followed by time spent in the sunshine.

Ingredients

- 1 cup cranberry juice
- 1/4 cup water
- 1/2 sliced lemon, rind included

Pour cranberry juice and water into small saucepan. Bring to simmer over medium heat. Add lemon and lower heat. Continue simmering, covered, for seven to ten minutes. Strain and transfer in pump-spray bottle or plastic plant spritzer. Apply to freshly cleaned, damp hair. If possible, sit with hair in sun for fifteen to twenty minutes. Otherwise, dry as usual. Without sun exposure, it will take repeated applications to notice lemon's light bleaching effect.

Storage and life span: Keep refrigerated. Will last seven to ten days.

SAGE TEA BRUNETTE

The ancient healing herb sage is frequently used in hair rinses to bring out the natural shine in brunette hair. As a natural darkener, it also will tone down brown hair a bit. With the addition of black tea, another hair darkener, this recipe will make medium-brown tones shimmer with dark, exotic highlights.

Ingredients

1 1/2 cups water
2 tablespoons dried sage leaves
5 bags black tea

Bring water to boil. Add sage and tea. Lower heat and allow to simmer, covered, for twenty minutes. Strain and transfer to pump-spray bottle or plastic plant spritzer. Apply to freshly cleaned, damp hair. Leave on hair for twenty minutes. Rinse well and dry as usual.

Storage and life span: Keep refrigerated. Will last seven to ten days.

GRAY-HAIR COVER-UP

Sooner or later, we all get them—those wiry silver or gray
strands of hair that stand out against our natural color. And, of
course, given enough time, these silver streaks take over.
Although there aren't many good homemade products that
cover gray 100 percent, you can use your own natural products
to blend those first strands as they begin to come in.

ROSEMARY-SAGE SOLUTION

Rosemary and sage are both natural hair darkeners that have
been used for centuries to even out brown hair tones as well as
to condition the scalp and hair shaft. To maintain the dark color
this rinse provides, use it every day or every other day.

Ingredients
1 1/2 cups water
  2 tablespoons rosemary
  2 teaspoons sage
  3 bags black tea

Bring water to boil. Add rosemary, sage, and tea. Lower heat
and allow to simmer, covered, for twenty minutes. Strain and
transfer to pump-spray bottle or plastic plant spritzer. Apply to
freshly cleaned, damp hair. Leave on for twenty minutes. Rinse
well and dry as usual.

Storage and life span: Keep refrigerated. Will last seven to
ten days.

Chapter 5

Nails: Strong and Shapely

One of the first things we notice about somebody when we meet them is their hands. Are they clean and well groomed, or do they appear worn and ragged? Since our hands, including our fingernails, are our most convenient tools, it's easy to understand how they could end up looking worn and ragged much of the time. Especially since our hard-working hands and nails, like our much abused feet, are often neglected during our usual beauty routine.

Beautiful nails are the hallmark of beautiful hands, but they definitely require a bit of effort to keep them beautiful. A healthful diet, complete with plenty of protein, is a good start. It's especially important to take care of your cuticles—that delicate area of skin that grows at the base of the nail bed. Softening and massaging this area not only keeps the cuticle from becoming dry, cracked, and inflamed, it also promotes nail growth. Also, although nails appear dead, they're constantly developing and building themselves up. It's important to give them proper care—much like the care you give your hair—to keep them shiny and healthy.

Unfortunately, commercial nail care can cost a fortune, with even the most basic manicures costing up to forty dollars a shot. Even over-the-counter nail products don't save much money once you buy all the products you need. The best solution is to make your own nail-care products at home. Although you'll still have to buy commercial polishes if you like a lot of color, you can make nail strengtheners, light shades, and cuticle-care products inexpensively in your own kitchen. If you do wear colored polish, keep your nails at their best by always giving them a chance to breathe every couple of weeks and by always wearing gloves when working with detergents and chemicals or while in the garden.

CUTICLE CARE

Healthy nail growth depends on healthy cuticles. Massaging your cuticles increases blood circulation in the nail area and promotes the growth of long, strong fingernails. Always remember, too, that you should never cut or bite your cuticles, or you risk infection. Instead, soften them with one of the following products, and then gently push them back with a cuticle stick.

OIL-YOLK CUTICLE SOFTENER

Lecithin-rich egg yolks are the perfect ingredient for conditioning and toning fingernail cuticles. Their fatty acids also will help keep fingernails and cuticles well moisturized, especially in dry seasons or climates. Olive oil is another excellent moisturizer and conditioner. And it helps lock in moisture so that your nails maintain that shiny, just-buffed look longer.

Ingredients
    1 egg yolk
    1 tablespoon olive oil

Combine egg yolk and olive oil in small mixing bowl. With fork or whisk, whip together until completely blended. Pour into shallow dish and soak nails for about fifteen minutes. Remove nails from mixture and lightly buff away excess mixture with cotton ball or tissue. Use as frequently as you like.

Storage and life span: Raw eggs spoil quickly. For best results, mix a fresh batch before each application. Leftover portion will last in the refrigerator for up to three days.

The Bees' Nails

Beeswax, the thick opaque substance that bees use to build honeycombs, is abundant in vitamins and minerals that benefit beauty products of all kinds. It is useful for conditioning the cuticle and nail and for creating a protective barrier that keeps the elements out and locks in moisture. A dash of peanut oil provides a delicious fragrance and adds yet another layer of protective moisture to the nail and cuticle.

Ingredients
2 teaspoons peanut oil
1 teaspoon grated beeswax

Combine oil and beeswax in heat-resistant glass measuring cup or mixing bowl. Place cup or bowl in about two inches of water in small saucepan on stove top (like double boiler) and bring to boil. Heat oil-beeswax mixture in homemade double boiler, stirring occasionally, until beeswax is melted. Stir well until mixture is completely blended. Remove from heat and pour into clean container. Allow to cool before using. Rub into cuticle and nail bed as frequently as you like.

Storage and life span: Store in a cool, dark place. Will last up to eight months.

COCOA BUTTER CUTICLE CARE

Cocoa butter is a favorite moisturizer in the tropics, where the relentless sun takes its toll on skin, hair, and nails. This rich conditioning agent will soften and condition your nails, leaving behind a silky coat that gives your nails a shiny and buffed look. Vitamin E oil helps prevent tissue breakdown and promotes healthy cell growth.

Ingredients
- 1   1,000 IUs vitamin E capsule, oil from
- /2   teaspoon grated cocoa butter

Combine vitamin E oil and cocoa butter in heat-resistant glass measuring cup or mixing bowl. Place cup or bowl in saucepan (like double boiler) containing about two inches of boiling water. Heat oil-cocoa butter mixture in homemade double boiler, stirring occasionally, until cocoa butter is melted. Stir well until mixture is completely blended. Remove from heat and pour into clean container. Allow to cool before using. Rub into cuticle and nail bed as needed.

Storage and life span: Store in a cool, dark place. Will last for four to six weeks.

PINEAPPLE-LEMON SOFTENER

Because pineapple juice contains a protein-digesting enzyme that helps remove layers of dead skin, it makes a wonderful cuticle softener and conditioner. Add a dash of lemon juice, which cleans, softens, and protects the cuticles and nails, and you have the perfect cuticle treatment. And it smells divine!

Ingredients

2 tablespoons pineapple juice
1/2 teaspoon lemon juice

Combine juices in clean bottle with lid. Shake well. Apply small amount to cuticles. Allow to work for ten to fifteen minutes. Rinse briefly with warm water. Use as often as necessary.

Storage and life span: Keep refrigerated when not in use. Will last for two to three weeks.

NAIL STRENGTHENERS

Hands down, the best nail strengthener is a healthful diet, complete with plenty of protein so that nails have all the nutrients they need to grow. Eating a well-balanced diet and drinking plenty of water also prevent your nails from drying out and becoming cracked and brittle. For added protection, especially if you live in harsh climates or work extensively with your hands, you can use topical nail strengtheners like the ones included in this section.

MEDITERRANEAN MAGIC

We know that Mediterranean women have beautiful skin, hair, and nails despite enduring the drying effects of the relentless sun. These women owe a great deal of their resilient beauty to the rich oils, such as almond and olive oil, that are abundant in their region. Both of these oils are rich in essential fatty acids that help restore flexibility and strength to dry, cracking, and peeling nails.

Ingredients
2   tablespoons olive oil
2   teaspoons almond oil

Combine oils in clean container with lid. Shake until well blended. Using fingertips or cotton swab, wipe small amount on entire fingernail. Allow to settle for three to five minutes. Use clean cloth or tissue to gently wipe away excess oil. Reapply as often as necessary.

Storage and life span: Store in a cool, dark place. Will last for two to three months.

SIMPLE ALOE SOLUTION

The clear sap of the spiny aloe plant may be one of the oldest
skin-healing ingredients used today. A soother of burns, cuts,
and abrasions, aloe vera also moisturizes, conditions, and aids
skin growth. Although the antiseptic witch hazel is generally
used as an oil-removing astringent, the few drops added to this
recipe simply help lift off excess oil, while keeping the nail bed
conditioned and healthy.

Ingredients

2 tablespoons aloe vera gel
3 drops witch hazel

Spoon aloe vera gel into small mixing bowl. Add witch hazel.
Using fork, stir two ingredients until smooth and well blended.
Transfer blended gel to clean container. Using fingertips or cotton
swab, wipe small amount on entire fingernail. If necessary, wipe
off excess gel with clean cloth or tissue. Use as often as needed.

Storage and life span: Store in a cool, dark place. Will last for
two to three months.

Honey of a Strengthener

Honey is one of nature's finest moisturizers, conditioners, and emollients. Rich with good-for-the-skin B-complex vitamins, this nectar from the bees also helps make dry nails healthy and flexible. Cocoa butter is another conditioning ingredient that helps revive moisture-depleted skin and nails. Petroleum jelly makes an excellent base for this nail cream, because it creates a protective barrier over the nail surface, locking in moisture.

Ingredients

- 1   teaspoon honey
- 3   tablespoons petroleum jelly
- 1/2   teaspoon grated cocoa butter

Combine ingredients in heat-resistant glass measuring cup or mixing bowl. Place cup or bowl in saucepan containing about two inches of boiling water (like double boiler). Heat mixture in homemade double boiler, stirring occasionally, until cocoa butter is melted and mixture is completely blended. Remove from heat and pour into clean container. Allow to cool before using. Rub on nails as needed.

Storage and life span: Store in a cool, dark place. Will last for two to three months.

NAIL OILS AND COLOR TREATMENTS

Traditional color nail polishes like the scarlet reds and deep purples that shimmer on the drugstore shelves are beyond the scope of this book. But that's not to say you can't make some pretty dazzling nail products of your own. You can create products that will leave your nails glistening a healthy white, that give them a touch of glitter, or that will add just the slightest hint of color.

LEMON-CHAMOMILE NAIL BRIGHTENER

Lemon juice has been used for centuries as a natural cleansing and bleaching ingredient. It can help create beautiful blonde streaks in naturally light hair and fade freckles and dark spots caused by the sun. It also can help brighten nails, especially those that have been darkened through the use of dark-colored nail polish. The fragrant chamomile flower is another gentle cleanser and lightener. Together, these two ingredients will leave your nails looking their natural best.

Ingredients
- 1/2 cup water
- 1 teaspoon chamomile herbal tea or dried flowers
- 2 tablespoons lemon juice

Add water to small saucepan and bring to boil on stove top. Remove from heat and add chamomile. Allow to steep for about ten minutes. Strain liquid into clean container with lid. Add lemon juice, close container, and shake well to mix. Allow to cool before using. Apply to nails with clean cotton swab or cotton ball. Use as needed, until nails are back to their natural color. Always apply nail oil after this treatment because lemon juice can dry out skin and nails. Shake before using.

Storage and life span: Refrigerate when not in use. Will last for two to three months.

NATURE'S SOFT RED TINT

If it's nail color you want, henna is the way to go. Though it won't put that shiny, enamel-like coating on your nails that you get from commercial nail polishes, it will dye your nails a more natural, soft red that won't begin to chip off in a matter of hours. Keep in mind, however, that since henna is a dye, you also won't be able to change the color. Rather, it will wear off after several weeks.

Ingredients

$1/4$ cup water
$1/4–1/2$ teaspoon red henna powder
        (depending on darkness desired)

Bring water to boil in small saucepan. Remove from heat and pour into small nonmetallic mixing bowl. Add henna powder and stir well, using wooden spoon or other nonmetallic stirring utensil. Pour into clean container. Apply to clean, dry nails with small paintbrush, taking care not to get on skin around nails. Always shake well before using.

Storage and life span: Store in a cool, dark place. Will last for two to three months.

EVENING GLITTER

This recipe is perfect for those special occasions when you want just a touch of sparkle. The glitter will wear off gradually as your nails lose moisture and become dry. But the effect will last long enough to shimmer throughout the evening. Just remember to apply the nail glitter last while getting ready, or you might end up with glitter where you don't want it.

Ingredients
1 tablespoon light olive oil
1/2 teaspoon silver (or colored) extra-fine glitter

In small clean container, mix olive oil and glitter. Stir or shake until glitter is evenly distributed throughout oil. Apply light coat on each nail with clean cotton swab, massaging oil into nail surface.

Storage and life span: It's best to mix a fresh batch before each occasion, but it will last for two to three months if stored in a cool, dark place.

BUFFED AND SHINY

Your nails will look their sharpest, healthiest best if you keep them well trimmed, clean, and buffed with a moisturizing buffing oil. This mixture of vitamin E oil and rich, nourishing almond and sunflower oils makes an ideal combination for soothing the cuticle area and moisturizing and conditioning the nail itself, while leaving behind a satiny, shiny finish.

Ingredients

1   800–1,000 IUs vitamin E capsules, oil from
1   teaspoon almond oil
1   teaspoon sunflower oil

Combine ingredients in clean container with lid. Shake or stir well to combine oils evenly. Using chamois or soft cotton cloth, rub oil into nails. Soak for about three to five minutes. Wipe off excess oil with clean cloth or tissue, buffing nails in process. Use as often as needed. Shake before using

Storage and life span: Store in a cool, dark place. Will last for two to three months.

HAND SOFTENERS

Generally speaking, the healthier your hands, the healthier your nails. Obviously, you should do your best to avoid exposing hands and nails to harsh chemicals and detergents by wearing gloves when working with these products. Gardening is another big culprit behind dry, cracked hands and nails. Investing in a pair of gardening gloves will go a long way toward saving your hands. Also, use a hand-softening lotion whenever possible after washing your hands to keep them soft and supple. Here are a couple to try.

NUTTY HAND SMOOTHER

Long before fancy commercial hand lotions were created, women around the world used straight cocoa butter to keep dishpan hands soft and supple. You can make this natural conditioner and emollient even more effective by adding a splash of apple cider vinegar, which helps maintain the healthy pH (acid/alkaline) balance in skin and controls excessive dryness and flakiness. The peanut oil in this recipe adds a powerful punch of nourishing vitamin E and will leave hands feeling silky and smooth.

Ingredients

  1 tablespoon peanut oil
  3 tablespoons grated cocoa butter
1 1/2 teaspoons apple cider vinegar

Combine oil and cocoa butter in heat-resistant glass measuring cup or mixing bowl. Place cup or bowl in saucepan containing about two inches of boiling water (like double boiler). Heat oil-cocoa butter in homemade double boiler, stirring occasionally, until cocoa butter is melted. Remove from heat and slowly add vinegar while blending with small whisk or fork. Pour creamy mixture into small container with airtight lid. Allow to cool before using.

Storage and life span: Store in a cool, dark place. Will last for eight months to a year.

Sunflower Softener

Big, bold sunflowers brim with scores of tiny seeds containing rich, light oil that is perfect for keeping skin nourished, moisturized, and conditioned. Beeswax—the opaque, creamy substance bees use to make their honeycombs—is chock-full of healthful B-complex vitamins. The lavender oil in this hand lotion revives tired muscles, acts as a mild antibacterial agent, and smells wonderful, too!

Ingredients
- 1/4 cup grated beeswax
- 1 tablespoon sunflower oil
- 5 drops lavender essential oil

Warm beeswax in small saucepan until melted. Add sunflower oil and remove from heat. Add lavender oil and beat mixture with whisk or fork until it is well blended and begins to cool. Pour into clean container with airtight lid. Allow to cool completely before using.

Storage and life span: Store in a cool, dark place. Will last for eight months to a year.

Chapter 6

A Dazzling Smile

You probably pay a lot of attention to your skin and hair, but well-cared-for teeth are even more important if you want to maintain a youthful, healthy appearance. Proper attention to your teeth will keep them whiter and brighter and in good working order. And by frequently brushing your teeth, you can help prevent receding gums, dental disease, and the premature loss of your teeth.

One of the things that troubles folks most about aging teeth is the change in color from pearly white to yellow or gray. Unfortunately, even brushing and flossing can't totally prevent this. Over the years, the nerves that nourish our teeth shrink, causing them to darken as they receive fewer nutrients. Also, as the enamel on our teeth—the white part—gets worn away with time, the yellow-tinged underlayer, called the dentin, becomes more visible.

Your first line of defense against discolored teeth is a good diet and exercise. The better you eat and the more you keep blood pumping to all parts of your body, the better nourished your teeth will be and the whiter they will stay. Also, be sure to get plenty of calcium to keep the bones that anchor your teeth to the jaw strong and sturdy. Your second line of defense is to watch what you put in your mouth. Acidic drinks such as carbonated sodas wear away precious pearly enamel before its time. And we all know how tobacco, coffee, and tea can stain teeth.

Currently, there are numerous commercial whitening and bleaching pastes and powders available to help reverse the yellowing process. Unfortunately, many of these are expensive, contain harsh chemicals, and produce questionable results. You're better off making your own dental-care products, using natural ingredients.

Finally, a fresh mouth is a healthy mouth. Homemade oral rinses and mouthwashes can keep your teeth, gums, and tongue clean and your breath fresh and sweet. Use them as often as you like—and don't forget to smile!

TOOTH POWDERS

Tooth powders are one of the least expensive and most effective alternatives to toothpaste you can make. They contain only natural ingredients, without all the harsh, abrasive additives, and they're perfect to take on a trip: simply pack a small, sealed container of powder in your cosmetic bag instead of toothpaste. And remember to brush your teeth at least twice a day for at least two to three minutes.

Cinnamon Baking Soda Scrub

Baking soda was one of the earliest dental hygiene products to hit the market at the turn of the century. Although it fell out of favor when fancy new gels and pastes took over the dental care industry, it recently has made a strong comeback, proving that newer isn't always better. Baking soda is a mild abrasive that thoroughly cleans teeth and gums, leaving your whole mouth feeling fresh and healthy. Since baking soda has a slightly bitter aftertaste that some people dislike, this recipe adds a dash of cinnamon, giving the powder a spicy flavor.

Ingredients
    4   tablespoons baking powder
1 1/2   teaspoons salt
  1/2   teaspoon cinnamon

Place ingredients in coffee grinder. Grind for about fifteen seconds, or until ingredients have consistency of finely blended powder. Transfer powder to jar with airtight lid. Sprinkle dash onto damp toothbrush and brush as usual.

Storage and life span: Store in a cool, dark, and dry place. Will last for six to eight months if the jar is sealed shut to keep out moisture.

Sage Tooth Whitener

Some folks say that all you have to do is rub a sage leaf across your teeth to keep them gleaming white. That's because sage contains natural tooth-whitening ingredients. Rather than just rubbing the leaves over your teeth, however, it's probably more effective if you grind them into a tooth powder like the one below.

Ingredients

- 2 tablespoons baking powder
- 2 teaspoons salt
- 2 teaspoons dried sage

Place ingredients in coffee grinder. Grind for about twenty seconds, or until ingredients have consistency of finely blended powder. Transfer powder to jar with airtight lid. Sprinkle dash onto damp toothbrush and brush as usual.

Storage and life span: Store in a cool, dark, and dry place. Will last for six to eight months if the jar is sealed shut to keep out moisture.

LICORICE TOOTH DELIGHT

If you like the taste of licorice, this unique tooth powder is for you. Adding a dash of anise seeds to baking soda and salt adds not only a little more cleaning abrasion but a cool, fresh licorice flavor as well. You don't need to overdo it with the anise. A little goes a long way.

Ingredients
- 3 tablespoons baking powder
- 1 teaspoon salt
- 1 pinch anise seeds

Place ingredients in coffee grinder. Grind for about twenty seconds, or until ingredients have consistency of finely blended powder. Transfer powder to jar with airtight lid. Sprinkle dash onto damp toothbrush and brush as usual.

Storage and life span: Store in a cool, dark, and dry place. Will last for six to eight months if the jar is sealed shut to keep out moisture.

Zesty Tooth Powder

It seems like every mouthwash, toothpaste, and breath freshener on the market contains some kind of mint—and with good reason. Mint is an astringent that leaves your mouth feeling cool and fresh. Cloves, too, are natural breath fresheners, although quite a bit warmer and spicier than mint leaves. Combined, these two create an herbal tooth powder that will leave your whole mouth tingly clean.

Ingredients

- 1 teaspoon baking powder
- 1 teaspoon dried mint
- 1 teaspoon dried clove
- 1/2 teaspoon salt

Place ingredients in coffee grinder. Grind for about twenty seconds, or until ingredients have consistency of finely blended powder. Transfer powder to jar with airtight lid. Sprinkle dash onto damp toothbrush and brush as usual.

Storage and life span: Store in a cool, dark, and dry place. Will last for six to eight months if the jar is sealed shut to keep out moisture.

ORAL RINSES

The best way to attack tooth decay and keep your teeth their brightest and whitest is to fight plaque from every angle. This means not just brushing and flossing but also using an oral rinse before brushing. This will kill bacteria and loosen dirt and tiny food particles so that they'll be completely swept away when you floss and brush. Plenty of oral rinses are available in drugstores, but studies show that you are probably just as well off saving your money and rinsing with simple homemade washes such as the following.

Salt-Ginger Rinse

Gathered from salt mines and the sea, salt is a natural antibacterial ingredient that kills germs in your mouth before you brush. Ginger's pungent, peppery flesh adds a spicy zip to this rinse, leaving your breath cool and clean for hours. This rinse tastes better when it's warm, so you may want to run the bottle under a stream of warm to hot water for a few seconds before using. Swish a small amount around your mouth and through your teeth for about fifteen seconds before brushing. As with any oral rinse, you should avoid swallowing it.

Ingredients
- 1 cup water
- 1 teaspoon sliced ginger
- 1 teaspoon salt

Bring water to boil in small saucepan on stove. Add ginger slices, reduce heat to low, and allow to simmer for about ten minutes. Strain ginger water through sieve into mixing bowl. Add salt and stir well, until dissolved. Transfer liquid to clean mouthwash bottle.

Storage and life span: Store in a cool, dark place. Will last for three to four weeks.

LEMON-VODKA ANTISEPTIC

Clean, clear, and astringent, vodka is an effective antiseptic. It helps loosen dirt and plaque before you brush. The lemon adds a nice, breath-freshening kick of flavor, and the fruit acids help dissolve built-up tartar on teeth. Swish a small amount of this rinse around your mouth and through your teeth for about fifteen seconds before brushing. Be careful not to swallow it.

Ingredients

1 cup water
1/2 sliced lemon, rind included
1/4 cup vodka

Bring water to boil in small saucepan on stove. Add lemon slices, reduce heat to low, and allow to simmer for about ten minutes. Strain lemon water through sieve into small mixing bowl. Add vodka and stir well. Transfer liquid to clean mouthwash bottle. Shake well before using.

Storage and life span: Keep refrigerated when not in use. Will last for six to eight weeks.

Raspberry Tartar Remover

Raspberries are rich in a mild fruit acid that can help remove tartar—a crusty plaque buildup—from the teeth. And, of course, they smell and taste simply delicious. The vodka in this recipe helps eliminate the germs caused by tooth disease before they can do their dirty work. This prebrushing rinse tastes almost good enough to drink. But, of course, you should not swallow it. Just swish a small amount around your mouth for about fifteen seconds before brushing.

Ingredients

- 1 cup water
- 1/4 cup fresh or frozen raspberries
- 2 tablespoons vodka

Boil water in small saucepan on stove. Add raspberries, reduce heat to low, and allow to simmer for about ten minutes. Strain raspberry water through sieve into small mixing bowl. Add vodka and stir well. Transfer liquid to clean mouthwash bottle. Shake well before using.

Storage and life span: For best results, keep refrigerated when not in use. Will last for six to eight weeks.

MOUTHWASHES

We all know that we should brush our teeth after every meal. But let's face it. In the real world, we're frequently eating on the run or far from our toothbrushes. Sometimes this isn't a big deal, as a few gulps of cool, clean water will make our mouths feel fresh enough until we get home. But sometimes a garlic-saturated pasta special or a steak smothered in onions can leave us longing for something to cleanse our palates. The following mouthwashes should do the trick.

ROSEMARY-CIDER MOUTHWASH

Originally found near the Mediterranean Sea, rosemary has been used in cosmetics for thousands of years. And rosemary charcoal has long been a popular tooth powder and cleanser. You can still use this aromatic herb to clean your mouth and freshen your breath. The combination of rosemary and apple cider vinegar makes this mouthwash a potent antiseptic that kills germs. As with oral rinses, mouthwashes are just for swirling around your mouth, not swallowing.

Ingredients

1 cup water
2 1/2 teaspoons dried rosemary
1/3 cup apple cider vinegar

Bring water to boil in small saucepan on stove top. Remove from heat and add rosemary. Cover and allow to steep for ten to fifteen minutes. Strain infusion into small mixing bowl and add vinegar. Mix well. Transfer to clean mouthwash bottle. Shake well before using.

Storage and life span: Store in a cool, dark place. Will last for six to eight weeks.

FINE THYME MOUTHWASH

The pungent, aromatic herb thyme is a powerful antiseptic and freshener. Combined with vodka, another powerful antiseptic, this mouthwash will freshen your breath and kill the bacteria that cause bad breath and tooth decay. Whenever your breath feels stale, swish a small amount throughout your mouth, but don't swallow it.

Ingredients

- 1 cup water
- 2 teaspoons thyme
- 1 tablespoon vodka

Bring water to boil in small saucepan on stove top. Remove from heat and add thyme. Cover and allow to steep for ten to fifteen minutes. Strain infusion into small mixing bowl and add vodka. Mix well. Transfer to clean mouthwash bottle. Shake well before using.

Storage and life span: Store in a cool, dark place. Will last for six to eight weeks.

BREATH FRESHENERS

All kinds of things can lead to bad breath. Maybe you've eaten too much garlic and onions. Maybe you have some minor indigestion. Maybe you've been on the run and missed your regular brushing. Even being slightly dehydrated can sour normally fresh breath. Of course, brushing your teeth or taking a hit of mouthwash can help fix problem breath, but as you know, when you're dashing around town, that's not always an option. You can buy commercial breath fresheners that taste like hard candies, but they're generally full of sugar and not the best for your teeth. Instead, make your own natural mouth fresheners to take along in your pocket or your purse, just in case.

PARSLEY BREATH PURIFIER

Parsley is a classic breath freshener. In fact, when all else fails, you can chew a sprig of this mildly spicy herb to cleanse your breath as well as to stimulate your digestion. Vodka and lemons are antiseptics and astringents that kill bacteria. The lemon rounds off the slightly pungent flavor of the parsley. Swish a small amount around your mouth whenever you think your breath needs help.

Ingredients

1   cup water
3   tablespoons fresh parsley
1   tablespoon vodka
3   drops lemon juice

Bring water to boil in small saucepan on stove top. Remove from heat and add parsley. Cover and allow to steep for about twenty minutes. Strain infusion into small mixing bowl. Add vodka and lemon juice. Mix well. Transfer to clean mouthwash bottle. Shake well before using.

Storage and life span: Store in a cool, dark place. Will last for six to eight weeks.

Fresh Mint Breath Spray

Cool, refreshing mint is the quintessential breath freshener. This aromatic herb acts as a mild antiseptic, killing germs that cause bad breath, and leaves a fresh, minty taste lingering in your mouth. Keep this breath spray stashed in your refrigerator, and take a little with you whenever you'll be away from home—and a toothbrush—for some time.

Ingredients
$1/2$ cup water
$1 1/2$ teaspoons dried peppermint leaves
$1/2$ teaspoon vodka

Bring water to boil in small saucepan on stove top. Remove from heat and add peppermint leaves. Cover and allow to steep for fifteen minutes. Strain mint-water into small jar with airtight lid and add vodka. Close jar and shake well. Pour small amount into miniature spray bottle to carry with you when you go out. Lightly spray your tongue and the sides of your mouth as necessary.

Storage and life span: Keep refrigerated when not in use. (The small amount you take with you will be fine for the day.) Will last for six to eight weeks.

CARRY-ALONG BREATH BOOSTERS

There are several things you can carry with you to chew whenever your breath needs a boost. Two of the most popular and effective are spicy cloves and dried ginger slices. For a double whammy against bad breath try the following recipe.

Ingredients

  10 fresh ginger slices
   3 dried cloves

Using mortar and pestle or handle of wooden spoon, crush cloves until powdered. Roll ginger slices in clove powder. Put coated slices in small paper bag and hang in dry, well-ventilated place (should dry in about a week). Store in small container, such as pill bottle, in your purse.

Storage and life span: Store in a cool, dark place. (If they're in your purse, keep your purse away from light.) Will last for eight to ten weeks.

Chapter 7

Unforgettable Fragrances

You may remember special events in your life by using your mind's eye to picture how everything and everyone looked the day you were married or the day you brought your new baby home. The reality, however, is that most people's memory for visual details is anything but 20/20. What is crystal clear is our memory for scents. The smell of chocolate chip cookies, your mother's favorite fragrance, or fresh-cut grass can take us back to the exact time and place we first encountered those aromas, sparking pleasant memories of days gone by.

Maybe that's why so many women (and men) throughout the ages have used perfumes and colognes: their personal scent made them unforgettable. Historians believe that people have used scents for at least 5,000 years. Dozens of famous figures in history, from Cleopatra to Napoleon, used special fragrances to increase their power and influence over the people they met.

The fact is, we're using fragrances the same way today. Why else would we break out our most expensive perfumes and colognes when we really want to impress? Unfortunately, those fragrances can cost a king's ransom at department stores. Just a few ounces of a favorite fragrance can cost fifty or a hundred dollars—or more!

That's why it pays, in more ways than one, to make your own fragrances. By using only natural ingredients, you'll save money, and the products are easy to make. Perhaps the best part is that you'll be creating your own "signature" fragrance. Talk about being truly unforgettable! This chapter will show you how to make a wide array of fragrances for both men and women. And as a bonus we'll help you pick the scents that work best for every occasion. A word of caution: Be careful not to splash these fragrances around your eyes or close to your genital area. Although they're fairly mild, most contain alcohol, which can sting sensitive skin.

TOILET WATERS

Toilet water may be the most enjoyable of all the fragrances to make and use at home. Light and clean-smelling, it's ideal for leaving behind just a hint of fragrance.

Liquid Lavender

We've always intuitively known it, but scientific research has now proven that certain scents can influence our sense of well-being—and lavender tops that list. Lavender actually increases the production of calming alpha waves in the brain, leaving people feeling more positive and less anxious. Now that's a nice way to start your day!

Ingredients
- 1 pinch dried lavender flowers
- 3/4 cup vodka
- 1 cup water
- 12 drops lavender essential oil

Combine lavender flowers and vodka in jar with airtight lid. Allow to sit for twenty-four hours, or at least overnight.

Strain lavender-vodka mixture to remove flower fragments. Combine with water and lavender oil and shake well.

Storage and life span: Store in a dark-colored glass bottle with a cork or other airtight lid. (Both light exposure and plastic can affect the scent.) Will last for six months if stored properly.

CITRUS SPRITZ

Citrus spitzes are among the nicest ways to wake up in the morning. Spritzing yourself with this fragrant blend after your morning glass of O.J. will leave you smelling clean and citrusy all day long, and it's actually good for you! Lemon oil tones and refreshes the skin and has an aroma that invigorates the mind. And oranges are rich in vitamin C, which is good for your skin.

Ingredients
    1   tablespoon dried orange peel
    1   teaspoon dried lemon peel
  1/2   teaspoon dried lime peel
  1/3   cup vodka
  1/2   cup water

Mix ingredients in glass jar with airtight lid. Leave in cool, dark place. Allow to sit for at least seven to ten days, or up to two weeks for stronger fragrance. Strain mixture to remove all bits of peel (coffee filters work well). Apply generously.

Storage and life span: Store in a dark-colored glass bottle with a cork or other airtight lid. (Both light exposure and plastic can affect the scent.) Will last for six months if stored properly.

Rosy Sunshine Scent

No other fragrance can match the timeless, classic scent of a rose. From Shakespeare to Bette Midler, poets, singers, and lovers have celebrated the rose's incredible beauty and rich fragrance. Because its aroma is particularly potent, however, too much of this flower's essence can be more overwhelming than wonderful. Adding just a few flakes of coconut will round out the floral fragrance with an earthy island aroma.

Ingredients

  1   cup dried rose petals (3 cups fresh petals)
  1/2   teaspoon dried coconut flakes
  1/2   cup vodka
  1/2   cup water

Mix ingredients in glass jar with airtight lid. Leave in cool, dark place. Allow to sit for at least seven to ten days, or up to two weeks for stronger fragrance. Strain mixture to remove petals and small flakes of coconut.

Storage and life span: Store in a dark-colored glass bottle with a cork or other airtight lid. (Both light exposure and plastic can affect the scent.) Will last for six months if stored properly.

Very Vanilla

Vanilla is our country's hands-down favorite flavor. We adore it in ice cream, cookies, cakes, custards, and frostings. And not only do we love the way vanilla tastes, we love the way it smells, too! In a groundbreaking study, both men and women found the aroma of vanilla more romantically enticing than even the most popular perfumes and colognes. Keep this recipe in mind for your next special night out.

Ingredients
5–6   drops vanilla extract
  1/4   cup vodka
  1/4   cup water

Combine ingredients in dark-colored glass bottle or jar with cork or other airtight lid. (Both light exposure and plastic can affect the scent.) Close lid tightly and shake well. Use generous amounts.

Storage and life span: Will last for six months if stored properly.

A Hint of Mint

Every restaurant knows that the cool, refreshing flavor of mint makes a great after-dinner pick-me-up as well as an effective breath freshener. What many people don't know, however, is that mint is also a wonderful morning eye-opener. Used in soaps, cosmetics, and cleansers, mint invigorates and stimulates the skin. And, although we don't often think of mint as a body fragrance, it will leave you smelling fresh, clean, and lightly spicy. This one's especially nice during the holiday season.

Ingredients

- 3 teaspoons fresh mint (or 3/4 teaspoon dried)
- 1/4 cup rubbing alcohol
- 1/3 cup water

Mix ingredients in glass jar with airtight lid. Leave in cool, dark place. Allow to sit for seven to ten days. Strain mixture to remove mint leaves. Apply liberally.

Storage and life span: Store in a dark-colored glass bottle or jar with a cork or other airtight lid. (Both light exposure and plastic can affect the scent.) Will last for up to six months if stored properly.

COLOGNES

Toilet waters and other light scents are ideal for leaving behind just a hint of fragrance to take you through the workday smelling fresh and clean. But when you're going out for a night on the town or to a special party, it's time to break out the cologne. Not as overwhelmingly potent as some perfumes (perfumes are too cumbersome for the scope of this book), colognes are the perfect fragrance for social gatherings. Here are a few to try.

JUST PEACHY

A member of the rose family, the fragrant peach is a favorite cologne scent, especially in the spring and summer months. To top it off, peach juice is actually good for your skin because it contains vitamins A and C. The warm, spicy aroma of cinnamon is a mental stimulant, and its earthy scent evens out the high fruity fragrance of the peach juice. The sweet almond oil adds a slightly nutty aroma and gives the cologne staying power.

Ingredients
- 1/2 peach, sliced
- 1/3 cup vodka or rubbing alcohol
- 2 drops essential cinnamon oil
- 1/4 teaspoon sweet almond oil

Combine peach slices and vodka or rubbing alcohol in small jar with airtight lid. Allow to sit for twenty-four hours. Strain mixture to remove peach slices. Mix in cinnamon and almond oils. Transfer to small dark-colored spray-top bottle, such as old-time perfume bottle. Shake well before using. Rub small amounts at "pulse" points: behind ears, on soft part of wrists and elbows, and on neck.

Storage and life span: Store excess in a dark-colored glass bottle or jar with a cork or other airtight lid. (Both light exposure and plastic can affect the scent.) Will last for six months if it is stored properly.

HERBAL DELIGHT

Sage is used around the world in cosmetics of all kinds. A member of the mint family, this fresh, fragrant herb is both stimulating and soothing. Chamomile is widely used for its healing powers, especially in fighting upset stomachs and in easing muscle aches when applied topically. Chamomile tea has long been used to soothe jangled nerves and as a sleep aid. The oils from this herb's golden flowers also give off a sweet, rich fragrance. The almond oil adds the aroma of nuts and gives the cologne staying power.

Ingredients
    1   teaspoon dried sage (2 teaspoons fresh, if possible)
    1   teaspoon chamomile
    1/3 cup vodka or rubbing alcohol
    1/4 teaspoon sweet almond oil

Combine sage, chamomile, and vodka or rubbing alcohol in glass jar with airtight lid. Leave in cool, dark place. Allow to sit for at least eight to ten days, or up to two weeks for stronger fragrance. Strain mixture to remove herb fragments (coffee filters work well). Add almond oil and transfer to small dark-colored spray-top bottle, such as old-time perfume bottle. Shake well before using. Rub or spray small amounts at "pulse" points: behind ears, on soft part of wrists and elbows, and on neck.

Storage and life span: Store excess in a dark-colored glass bottle or jar with a cork or other airtight lid. (Both light exposure and plastic can affect the scent.) Will last for six months if stored properly.

Lemon Day Spray

Lemon may be the ultimate daytime cologne. Fresh, clean, and highly fragrant, the delightful scent of this tart citrus fruit provides an invigorating mental kick throughout the day. Originating in Southeast Asia, lemons smell so delightful they are used in everything from dishwashing detergents and soap powders to bath soaps and facial cleansers.

Ingredients

   1   small lemon peel
   1/3   cup vodka or rubbing alcohol
   2   tablespoons water
   1/4   teaspoon castor oil

Combine lemon peel and vodka or rubbing alcohol in glass jar with airtight lid. Leave in cool, dark place. Allow to sit for at least eight to ten days, or up to two weeks for stronger fragrance. Strain mixture to remove bits of peel. Add water and castor oil and transfer to small dark-colored spray-top bottle, such as old-time perfume bottle. Shake well before using. Rub or spray small amounts at "pulse" points: behind ears, on soft part of wrists and elbows, and on neck.

Storage and life span: Store excess in a dark-colored glass bottle or jar with a cork or other airtight lid. (Both light exposure and plastic can affect the scent.) Will last for six months if stored properly.

ISLAND ROMANCE

Pungent and spicy, ginger root is a tropical favorite for stir-fries, beverages, desserts, and home remedies; it also is used cosmetically as an antiseptic for oily skin. Vanilla has a rich aroma that adds a sweet note to the spicy smell of ginger. Together, these two make a delicious, unforgettable fragrance that will leave you smelling good enough to eat!

Ingredients

1 teaspoon sliced fresh ginger root
1/3 cup vodka or rubbing alcohol
3–4 drops vanilla extract
2 tablespoons water
1/4 teaspoon sweet almond oil

Combine ginger root and vodka or rubbing alcohol together in glass jar with airtight lid. Leave in cool, dark place and allow to sit for at least eight to ten days, or up to two weeks for stronger fragrance. Strain mixture to remove ginger fragments (coffee filters work well). Add vanilla extract, water, and almond oil. Transfer to small dark-colored spray-top bottle, such as old-time perfume bottle. Shake well before using. Rub or spray small amounts at "pulse" points: behind ears, on soft part of wrists and elbows, and on neck.

Storage and life span: Store excess in a dark-colored glass bottle or jar with an airtight top. (Both light exposure and plastic can affect the scent.) Will last for six months if stored properly.

Night Magic

Nighttime calls for a special kind of fragrance all its own. The perfect scent should be spicy, rich, and slightly mysterious. This cologne, infused with cloves and cinnamon oil, is ideal for evening wear. It also makes a perfect cologne for the holidays, when spiced rum and gingersnaps are the order of the day.

Ingredients

- 2 cloves, crushed
- 1 cinnamon stick, broken in pieces
- 1/3 cup vodka or rubbing alcohol
- 3 tablespoons water
- 1–2 drops cinnamon oil
- 1/4 teaspoon sweet almond oil

Combine cloves, cinnamon stick, and vodka or rubbing alcohol in glass jar with airtight lid. Leave in cool, dark place. Allow to sit for at least eight to ten days, or up to two weeks for stronger fragrance. Strain mixture to remove herb fragments (coffee filters work well). Add water and cinnamon and almond oils and transfer to small dark-colored spray-top bottle, such as old-time perfume bottle. Shake well before using. Rub or spray small amounts at "pulse" points: behind ears, on soft part of wrists and elbows, and on neck.

Storage and life span: Store excess in a dark-colored glass bottle or jar with a cork or other airtight lid. (Both light exposure and plastic can affect the scent.) Will last for up to six months if stored properly.

SCENTED POWDERS

Nothing finishes off a bath or a shower like the silky smoothness of a fine dusting powder. Powders help prevent chafing in tender areas and keep you dry in humid conditions. They also can be scented to leave just a touch of fragrance on your skin. Scented powders are wonderfully inexpensive and easy to make with ingredients you probably already have in your kitchen. Here are a couple to try.

Sweet Vanilla Dusting

The fragrance of the delicious vanilla bean is almost universally admired for use in cosmetics and fragrances all over the world. This dusting powder will leave you smelling sweet and clean throughout the day.

Ingredients
$1^1/2$ cups cornstarch
$1^1/2$ teaspoons vanilla extract
   1 teaspoon sunflower oil

Place cornstarch in small plastic container. Add vanilla extract and sunflower oil. Close container and shake gently but thoroughly until powder and liquids are completely mixed. Apply with powder puff or transfer to shaker-top powder container. Apply liberally on freshly towel-dried skin.

Storage and life span: Will last up to twelve months if kept dry.

CINNAMON-ORANGE BATH POWDER

When you're in the mood for something a little on the spicy side, reach for this zesty bath powder. Infused with oils from the sweet orange and the aromatic spice cinnamon, this is the perfect powder for dusting up to go out on the town.

Ingredients

$1\frac{1}{2}$ cups cornstarch
  4 drops cinnamon oil
2–3 drops orange essential oil
  1 teaspoon sunflower oil

Place cornstarch in small plastic container. Add cinnamon, orange oil, and sunflower oil. Close container and shake gently but thoroughly until powder and liquids are completely mixed. Apply with powder puff or transfer to shaker-top powder container. Apply liberally on freshly towel-dried skin.

Storage and life span: Will last up to twelve months if kept dry.

YOUR PERSONAL SCENT WARDROBE

Everything changes. The styles we wear, the foods we eat, even where we live will probably vary over the years. So why should our fragrances remain the same? Yet many women get stuck in a rut when it comes to buying toilet waters and colognes—always seeming to choose florals or spicy musks. Like purses, scarves, and shoes, your scent can complement specific settings. Here's a quick guide for selecting the right scent for the right occasion.

At the office: Light, fresh fragrance of lemon, lavender, peach, or mint.

Casual party: Fun fragrance of coconut, pine, sage, chamomile, or basil.

Dinner dates: Slightly romantic fragrance of rose, violet, lilac, or orchid.

Formal night out: Daring, spicy fragrance of cloves, cinnamon, ginger, or sandalwood.

Outdoor activities: Natural and sweet-smelling fragrance of vanilla, orange, or jasmine.

Chapter 8

Massage Magic

Once regarded as a luxury reserved for the wealthy spa-goer, massage has been working its way into the mainstream culture as an effective way to relieve stress, heal sore muscles, and even improve skin tone.

At the most basic level, massage oils make the skin smooth and slick, so that your hands easily glide over the muscles. But massage oils are more than just skin lubricants. They also contain healing ingredients such as essential oils from flowers and herbs that penetrate the skin and work their way down into muscles. Unfortunately, although these fragrant oils can relieve the pain of sore muscles, they also can put a serious dent in your wallet.

The best option is simply to make your own. You'll not only save money, you'll also develop oils to match your personal scent and medicinal preferences. And homemade massage oils make great gifts!

In this chapter you'll find a sampling of oils for all your massage needs. Once you've mastered these recipes, try experimenting with your own creations. The possibilities are endless.

ESSENTIAL MASSAGE OILS

Massage has been credited with healing ailments of all kinds, from basic overused muscles and stress headaches to menstrual cramps and insomnia. Most of the healing, of course, is in the hand motion. But there's little doubt that massage oils play a role, too. In "An Introduction to Aromatherapy" (p. 164) you will find help in deciding which herbal essence to use for which ailment.

Sweet Skin and Muscle Relief

Long used for medicinal purposes throughout Europe, the golden-blonde chamomile flower is a healthful, fragrant massage oil ingredient. Not only is chamomile soothing and healing to the muscles, it also cleanses and refreshes pores, which leads to a total-body rejuvenation. Fragrant purple lavender flowers are used around the world to soothe tired, sore muscles and to relieve stress-related headaches. This luxurious combination guarantees a wonderfully sweet-smelling, relaxing massage.

Ingredients
2/3   cup sunflower oil
1–2   drops lavender essential oil (optional)
2   teaspoons fresh lavender
2   teaspoons chamomile herbal tea

Pour sunflower oil into canning jar or other wide-mouthed glass container. Mix in lavender oil, if using, fresh lavender, and chamomile. Cover tightly. Allow to sit in cool, dark place for ten to fourteen days. Strain to remove herb fragments. Funnel into clean, sterile squeeze container, such as those used for suntan lotions, or into small glass cork-topped bottle. Alternate method: Combine ingredients in small saucepan and gently heat for five to ten minutes *without allowing oil to simmer or boil.* Cool completely and then strain to remove fragments. Pour into container of choice.

Storage and life span: Store in a cool, dark place. Should keep for about nine months.

LEMONY GINGER TENSION RELIEVER

Spicy, pungent ginger is a wonderful circulation stimulant that will make your muscles feel alive and vibrant after a good rub-down. It's also a wonderful antiseptic for the skin that will help clear up any skin conditions you may have. Lemon is a favorite ingredient in cosmetics of all kinds. Used as a massage oil, it helps lift off dead skin cells, leaving your body looking soft and clean.

Ingredients
- 2/3 cup safflower oil
- 1/2 teaspoon freshly sliced ginger root
- 1/2 Sliced rind from lemon
- 1 pinch basil (fresh or dried)

Pour oil into canning jar or other wide-mouthed glass container. Mix in ginger root, lemon rind, and basil. Cover tightly. Allow to sit in cool, dark place for eight to ten days. Strain to remove herb fragments. Store in glass cork-topped bottle or clean shampoo bottle. Alternate method: Combine ingredients in small saucepan and gently heat for five to ten minutes *without allowing oil to simmer or boil.* Cool completely and then strain to remove fragments. Pour into container of choice.

Storage and life span: Store in a cool, dark place. Should keep for about nine months.

VANILLA-NUTMEG ROMANCE

It would be hard to find anything that smells sweeter or more romantic than the old-fashioned fragrance of vanilla. Add the spicy kick of nutmeg and you have the perfect massage oil for a romantic evening. In fact, studies have shown that men find the scent of baked goods, like those containing vanilla and nutmeg, more arousing than most perfumes or colognes. Keep that in mind the next time you're looking for an amorous night with your spouse!

Ingredients
- 2/3 cup sunflower oil
- 5–7 drops vanilla extract
- 1/2 teaspoon nutmeg powder

Pour oil, vanilla extract, and nutmeg powder into small ceramic mixing bowl. Stir well. Transfer oil to clean, sterile squeeze container, such as those used for suntan lotions, or to a small glass cork-topped bottle.

Storage and life span: Store in a cool, dark place. Should keep for about nine months.

Orange-Cinnamon Revival

Oranges not only have a zesty, refreshing fragrance, they're also brimming with vitamin C, which helps heal, exfoliate, and rejuvenate the skin. These rich, citrusy fruits also leave your skin feeling soft and clean. And spicy, exotic cinnamon adds a rich, earthy note to this sexy massage oil.

Ingredients
- 2/3 cup sweet almond oil
- 1/2 sliced rind from orange
- 1 cracked cinnamon stick

Pour oil into canning jar or other wide-mouthed glass container. Mix in orange rind and cinnamon stick. Cover tightly. Allow to sit in cool, dark place for seven to ten days. Strain oil to remove peel and cinnamon fragments. Transfer oil to clean, sterile squeeze container, such as those used for suntan lotions, or to glass cork-topped bottle. Alternate method: Combine ingredients in small saucepan and gently heat for five to ten minutes *without allowing oil to simmer or boil.* Cool completely and then strain to remove fragments. Pour into container of your choice.

Storage and life span: Store in a cool, dark place. Should keep for about nine months.

Three-Herb Massage

Rosemary has been used for centuries as a tonic to improve memory. Sage cleanses the skin and invigorates the muscles. And thyme has long been used as a medicinal panacea for conditions of all kinds. Although it may not cure everything that ails you, it is a wonderful skin antiseptic. All three of these herbs are rich, fragrant, and relaxing.

Ingredients

- 2/3 cup extra-light olive oil
- 2 teaspoons fresh rosemary
- 2 teaspoons fresh sage
- 1/2 teaspoon fresh thyme

Pour oil into canning jar or other wide-mouthed glass container. Mix in rosemary, sage, and thyme. Cover tightly. Allow to sit in cool, dark place for ten to fourteen days. Strain to remove herb fragments. Funnel into clean, sterile squeeze container, such as those used for suntan lotions, or into small glass cork-topped bottle. Alternate method: Combine ingredients in small saucepan and gently heat for five to ten minutes *without allowing oil to simmer or boil.* Cool completely and then strain to remove fragments. Pour into container of choice.

Storage and life span: Store in a cool, dark place. Should keep for about nine months.

INSTANT MASSAGE

Reviving, refreshing, and invigorating, peppermint oil is one of the most stimulating massage oils you can use. You can make this clean, energizing oil in just seconds by mixing peppermint essential oil with a vegetable-oil base. Here's how.

Ingredients

$2/3$ cup sunflower oil

2–3 drops peppermint essential oil

Combine oils and pour in plastic squeeze container, such as those used for suntan lotions, or in glass cork-topped bottle. Use liberally.

Storage and life span: Store in a cool, dark place. Should keep for about nine months.

SORE-MUSCLE SOLUTIONS

Whether you ran a challenging 5K race over the weekend or spent the day pulling weeds and lugging laundry, you know the pain of overused muscles that just don't want to move anymore. Though rubbing tired arm, leg, and back muscles with just about anything would make them feel better, you can heal them more quickly with massage oils designed especially for reviving tired muscle tissue. Try these the next time you overdo it.

ROSEMARY RUB

Originating in the Mediterranean region, the herb rosemary is a fragrant member of the mint family. The ancient Romans believed that eating this herb could improve memory and ward off disease. It's also been fabled to keep evil spirits at bay when burned. Although we can't be sure about all that, rosemary essence is a nice remedy for headaches. It also improves circulation and helps soothe tired, sore muscles when used topically.

Ingredients

2/3 cup safflower oil

1 1/2 tablespoons fresh rosemary

1–2 drops rosemary essential oil (optional)

Pour safflower oil into canning jar or other wide-mouthed glass container. Mix in fresh rosemary and rosemary oil, if using. Cover tightly. Allow to sit in cool, dark place for ten to fourteen days. Strain oil to remove herb fragments. Funnel oil into clean, sterile squeeze container, such as those used for suntan lotions, or into small glass cork-topped bottle. Alternate method: Combine ingredients in small saucepan and gently heat for five to ten minutes *without allowing oil to simmer or boil.* Cool completely and then strain to remove fragments. Pour into container of choice.

Storage and life span: Store in a cool, dark place. Should keep for about nine months.

Eucalyptus Soother

Eucalyptus may be the finest of the essential oils when it comes to sore-muscle relief. Highly aromatic, eucalyptus not only alleviates fatigue and reduces the pain caused by muscle strain, it also revives a tired mind. For some really special pampering, treat yourself to a eucalyptus bath. Just add two or three drops of eucalyptus essential oil to your bath before your eucalyptus oil massage.

Ingredients
  1   cup sunflower oil
  1/4 cup fresh eucalyptus leaves

Pour oil into canning jar or other wide-mouthed glass container. Mix in eucalyptus. Cover tightly. Allow to sit in cool, dark place for ten to fourteen days. Strain oil to remove herb fragments. Funnel oil into clean, sterile squeeze container, such as those used for suntan lotions, or into small glass cork-topped bottle. Alternate method: Combine ingredients in small saucepan and gently heat for five to ten minutes *without allowing oil to simmer or boil.* Cool completely and then strain to remove fragments. Pour into container of choice.

Storage and life span: Store in a cool, dark place. Should keep for about nine months.

AN INTRODUCTION TO AROMATHERAPY

Real estate brokers have known the benefits of aroma-therapy for years. Want to sell a house quickly? Have a fresh batch of cookies baking in the oven when you show it. The warm, heavenly aroma will transport potential buyers back to a pleasant place from their childhood. They'll associate that cozy feeling with your home, and bingo, you've sold your house!

Although aromatherapy has been in the spotlight lately, it's anything but new. Religious ceremonies throughout the ages have included the burning of special incense as part of their sacred rites. And European doctors in the eleventh century often used essential oils to help prevent and to heal disease.

It's only recently, however, that researchers have discovered what our ancestors seemed to know instinctively all along: certain aromas are more than just pleasant to our noses. They can actually alter our brain waves, which in turn can profoundly affect our moods. Scents can make us more alert. They can calm us down. They can lift our spirits. They may even be able to stimulate our immune systems. Scientists can actually study the different parts of the brain that each scent affects. Orange, jasmine, and rose, for example, alter brain waves in a way that produces calming sensations and increases your sense of well-being, while oils like rosemary and black pepper are more stimulating and increase your energy response. Because they're so good for you in so many ways, many of the recipes in this book call for a drop or two of essential oils of all kinds.

Ever wonder why one whiff from a bakery, a hay field, or a familiar aftershave can open the floodgates for long-forgotten memories? It's because the olfactory nerve—the one found in the upper regions of the nasal cavity—provides the shortest, most direct route to your limbic system, the brain's emotional mainframe and the warehouse for stored memories. The limbic system also is directly connected to those parts of the brain that control your heart rate, blood pressure, breathing, memory, stress levels, and hormone balance. No wonder many holistic health practitioners incorporate aromatherapy into their practices.

As if that weren't enough, you also can use many of these fragrant healers topically. For example, their astringent, antiseptic properties make them good killers of infectious germs on cuts and abrasions on the skin. They also are great for nourishing mature, dry, or cracked skin.

If you're new to aromatherapy, however, you're best off exercising caution when applying oils to your skin. For one thing, most of them are very strong and should be diluted with water before application. They also can cause allergic skin reactions, particularly among people with fair skin or freckled complexions. If you want to use an essential oil topically, perform a skin test first. Simply place a drop of the oil on a cotton swab and dab it on the inside of your wrist or inner elbow. Cover it up and keep it unwashed for twenty-four hours. If you don't experience any itching, redness, or rash, you should be able to use the oil topically. Caution: Pregnant women should not use any oils topically.

You can buy essential oils at many pharmacies. But you'll often end up paying a lot of money for a little bit of oil. Instead, you can make your own essential oils by soaking herbs, flowers, or roots in vodka or rubbing alcohol for ten to fourteen days. You then pour a small amount of the oil in a potpourri burner and enjoy the effects. The following primer will guide you through the most commonly used essences and their best uses.

Basil: A favorite in recipes of all kinds, basil is uplifting and refreshing. Using basil in a bath is popular in Ayurvedic medicine for cooling and warming the skin simultaneously. It also may be used as a bug repellent.

Black pepper: Though inhaling too much at once can make you sneeze, black pepper is good for increasing energy levels. It's derived from the unripe fruit and berry of the peppercorn.

Cedarwood: Popularly used to scent wardrobes and dresser drawers, cedarwood is a sweet fragrance that clears the mind. Some people use it topically to relieve itchy skin. It is also an astringent for oily skin.

Citrus oils: The next time you come home growling from a bad day at work, diffuse some citrus essence into the air. Citrus oils can chase away foul moods and create a bright, uplifting atmosphere. Orange, lemon, lime, or grapefruit will do the trick.

Clary sage: Another fine herb for combating depression, menstrual pain, and premenstrual syndrome. When diffused into the air or used as a massage oil, this essence is said to make you feel euphoric.

Eucalyptus: Popularly used in cold and flu chest rubs and cough drops, eucalyptus helps clear stuffiness and congestion. It's also a classic antiviral and expectorant essence in aromatherapy.

Floral oils: We love the way flowers look. And we love the way they smell. Hands down, floral oils are the best for stress relief. They're also the fragrances that people tend to like best. Experiment with flower essences of all kinds from the most basic rose to exotic wildflowers.

Geranium: Geranium is among the floral essences that relax you. It also has special properties as an antiviral and antifungal agent. It's gentle on the skin and works well topically.

Lavender: The queen of essential oils, lavender may be the most healing of all the fragrances. Researchers in hospital intensive care units have found that this sweet essence can improve moods and relieve stress. It also comes to the rescue as an anti-septic for minor injuries such as small burns, cuts, bruises, and insect bites. Because it contains a lot of ester, it has an almost sedative quality. Some people add a drop or two on their bed sheets to relieve brief bouts of insomnia.

Mandarin: Made from the sweet mandarin orange, this citrus essence is one of the most popular for alleviating anxiety and for lifting bad moods.

Patchouli: Very popular in the days of Woodstock, this spicy, pungent essential oil is used to calm and focus the mind. Patchouli also soothes dry skin. Some folks say it even works as an aphrodisiac.

Peppermint: Cool and invigorating, peppermint is popularly used to relieve symptoms of cold, flu, and sinus congestion. Just place two or three drops of peppermint essence in a bowl of hot water and inhale. Peppermint also is a great mental stimulant.

Rose: A classic in the world of aromatherapy, rose oils are cherished for relieving stress and elevating moods.

Rosemary: A longtime culinary favorite in Mediterranean countries, rosemary has a fresh aroma that soothes frazzled nerves and relieves anxiety.

Sandalwood: Derived from the sandalwood tree, sandal-wood oil is used in baths to keep the immune system running at peak condition. Sandalwood oil also can act as an antiseptic.

Spearmint: Like its sister essence peppermint, spearmint energizes the mind when inhaled. It also is cool and invigorat-ing when used topically. Spearmint is especially effective as an astringent for oily skin.

Tea tree: Acting as a gentle antiseptic, tea tree oil is used commonly for skin conditions such as burns, cold sores, and athlete's foot as well as for lip balms, soaps, and dental products. Tea tree oil also is an effective antibacterial and antifungal agent.

Ylang-ylang: One of the more exotic floral essences, ylang-ylang is widely regarded for its ability to soothe the body physically and mentally.

Chapter 9

For Your Feet

No other body part takes the abuse that your feet take. These earthbound appendages support your weight all day long on hard surfaces of all kinds. To make matters worse, we're not very kind to our feet. Although they'd like to spend the day in cushy, well-supported sneakers, they generally end up crammed into fashionable shoes with pointy toes, high heels, and no support. The result is sore, tired foot muscles, bunions, corns, calluses, and a host of other foot problems.

The first and most obvious solution is to be nicer to your feet by wearing well-fitting, comfortable shoes. But since that's not always possible, it's important to pamper your feet occasionally to reduce some of the wear and tear and to protect them from injury.

Try immersing your tired feet in an invigorating footbath at the end of a long day. Remove corns and calluses with a home-made pumice stone. Dust your feet with fragrant, antiseptic foot powders. And massage your weary foot muscles with special reviving oils. These are all products you can make simply and affordably in your own home. Try them. Your feet will thank you!

CORN AND CALLUS REMOVERS

If you wear lots of high-heeled, pointy-toed professional pumps, then you're probably familiar with foot problems such as corns and calluses. Although these shoes look pretty, what they do to our feet is anything but. Corns are the thickened clumps of dead skin cells that form on the top of or in between your toes. They occur over time as the top of your toes rub against the tight-fitting toe box in most women's shoes. Calluses are another type of dead-cell buildup that generally occur on the bottoms of feet. Calluses are usually the result of pounding too much pavement without enough padding beneath your feet. Corns and calluses not only look unattractive, they also can be painful. A professional pedicure can take care of these foot afflictions, but unfortunately they can be prohibitively expensive. A better idea is to make some personal foot-care products at home. Here are a few to try.

ONION CORN REMOVER

Onions have long been used as poultices for conditions ranging from respiratory disorders to skin diseases. Here the humble onion comes to the rescue for one of the most common foot problems: corns. Used as a poultice, the onion has healing components that will penetrate the skin and soften the corn to help remove it more quickly.

Ingredients
 1/4 small onion, minced
  1   tablespoon oil
 1/4 cup baby shampoo
  1   clean bandanna or handkerchief

Sauté onion in oil until transparent. Strain onion in sieve or sifter. Combine baby shampoo and onion in small mixing bowl. Mix well. While mixture is warm, pour small amount on bandanna or handkerchief. Fold bandanna or handkerchief closed and apply to corn for ten to fifteen minutes. Store unused mixture in small plastic container with lid. Warm in microwave or on stove top before using again.

Storage and life span: Use every day until the corn is diminished. Will last only two to three days.

Fresh Pumice Exfoliater

Pumice stones are similar to the gentlest sandpaper in treating your roughened feet. Used regularly, they remove tough, dead skin from the soles of feet and from the tops of toes, exposing baby-soft skin underneath. This recipe includes sunflower oil for extra softening power as well as a few drops of lavender oil to give your feet a fresh, sweet aroma.

Ingredients
   1/3 cup sunflower oil
   3   drops lavender essential oil
   1   small pumice stone

Combine sunflower oil and lavender oil in small mixing bowl. Submerge pumice stone in mixture and soak for twenty to thirty minutes. In the meantime, soak feet for a few minutes. When time is up, remove stone from mixture and blot away extra moisture. Rub callused areas in circular motion, using small amount of pressure. Repeat several times a week.

Storage and life span: Store unused mixture in a small plastic container with lid. Will last for six months.

Sea Salt Solution

Coarse sea salt is a great treatment for many foot ailments. As a rub, the grains of salt exfoliate dead skin cells and smooth out corn and callus buildups. Salt also acts as an antiseptic that kills the germs and bacteria that attack your feet every day. The vinegar in this recipe acts as a skin softener. The eucalyptus oil improves circulation and helps wipe out traces of foot odor, leaving your feet smelling fresh and clean.

Ingredients

3   tablespoons sea salt
1   tablespoon apple cider vinegar
4   drops eucalyptus essential oil

In small mixing bowl, combine sea salt, vinegar, and eucalyptus oil. Mix well until sea salt crystals are slightly softened. Wet feet in warm footbath. Dip washcloth in warm water. Pour sea salt mixture on washcloth and gently rub bottoms of feet and tops of toes as needed.

Storage and life span: Because the salt will eventually dissolve completely, this product cannot be reused. Make a new batch before each rubdown or bath.

SOOTHING FOOTBATHS

Short of a foot massage, nothing makes your tired feet feel more invigorated than soaking them in a steamy, warm footbath. Although plain water does the trick in a pinch, you can make your footbaths even more effective by infusing them with herbs that relax muscles, increase circulation, and help kill the germs that are the source of skin problems, such as athlete's foot. Try these recipes the next time your aching feet need a little TLC.

Eucalyptus Foot Energizer

Eucalyptus is an ancient, aromatic plant, long recognized for its many healing properties. Often used to relieve congestion caused by respiratory conditions of all kinds, eucalyptus also helps heal muscle strain. The essential oils found in the eucalyptus plant can offset fatigue and soothe minor strain, leaving you energized and revived. The peppercorns add a warming sensation to the bath and also promote circulation, which hastens muscle healing.

Ingredients
   1 gallon steaming water
      (add more if needed to submerge your feet)
   1 handful dried eucalyptus
   1 teaspoon whole peppercorns
 2–3 drops eucalyptus essential oil

Pour hot water into footbath or other heat-resistant container large enough to accommodate both feet. Add eucalyptus, peppercorns, and eucalyptus oil. Steep ingredients in water for few minutes, stirring occasionally. When water is comfortable to touch, submerge feet. Sit back and soak for fifteen to twenty minutes. Dry feet thoroughly when finished, making sure to dry between toes. Wear heavy socks to keep feet warm.

Storage and life span: This recipe is good for one footbath only. Make a new batch before each bath.

Cool Mint Foot Relief

Stimulating and invigorating, mint improves circulation in your feet, reviving and healing worn-out muscles. The Lifesavers in this recipe add a touch of sugar, which helps soften the hard, rough skin on your feet, leaving them smooth and soft to the touch. The super-minty aroma of this recipe will revive your mind as well as your feet.

Ingredients
- 1 gallon steaming water
  (add more if needed to submerge your feet)
- 1/2 cup fresh mint
- 1–2 peppermint or wintergreen Lifesavers

Pour hot water into footbath or other heat-resistant container large enough to accommodate both feet. Add mint and Lifesavers. Allow ingredients to steep in water for few minutes, stirring occasionally. When water is comfortable to touch, submerge feet. Soak for fifteen to twenty minutes. Dry feet thoroughly when finished, making sure to dry between toes. Wear heavy socks to keep feet warm.

Storage and life span: This recipe is good for one footbath only. Make a new batch before each bath.

Ocean Lavender Footbath

Derived from the saline waters of the sea, sea salt is soothing and energizing when used in a footbath. It is especially beneficial if you have problems with skin infections or sore, cracked skin. The lavender in this recipe adds skin-healing power of its own and provides essential oils that revive sore, tired muscles. As an added bonus, lavender acts as a gentle deodorant to keep your feet smelling fresh.

Ingredients
- 1 gallon steaming water
  (add more if needed to submerge your feet)
- 1/3 cup dried lavender
- 4–5 drops lavender essential oil
- 2 tablespoons sea salt

Pour hot water into footbath or other heat-resistant container large enough to accommodate both feet. Add lavender, lavender oil, and sea salt. Allow ingredients to steep in water for a few minutes, stirring occasionally. When water is comfortable to touch, submerge feet. Relax and soak for fifteen to twenty minutes. Dry feet thoroughly when finished, making sure to dry between toes. Wear heavy socks to keep feet warm.

Storage and life span: This recipe is good for one footbath only. Make a new batch before each bath.

CHAMOMILE-THYME FOOT SOAK

This is the perfect bedtime footbath. Native to western Europe, chamomile has been used cosmetically and medicinally for centuries. It is perhaps most widely used as a tea to help people sleep when they have minor bouts of insomnia. It also can help reduce minor muscle pain, sore feet, or general fatigue. The thyme in this recipe helps improve circulation and calm your nerves. The salt is a skin soother that will leave your feet feeling soft and pampered.

Ingredients

- 1 gallon steaming water
  (add more if needed to submerge your feet)
- 1/4 cup dried chamomile
- 1/4 cup dried thyme
- 1 teaspoon salt

Pour hot water into footbath or other heat-resistant container large enough to accommodate both feet. Add chamomile, thyme, and salt. Allow ingredients to steep in water for a few minutes, stirring occasionally. When water is comfortable to touch, submerge feet. Sit back and soak for fifteen to twenty minutes. Dry feet thoroughly when finished, making sure to dry between toes. Wear heavy socks to keep feet warm.

Storage and life span: This recipe is good for one footbath only. Make a new batch before each bath.

REVIVING FOOT RUBS

We don't tend to think of our feet as particularly muscular like our backs or shoulders, but if you think about how much weight our feet support each and every day, you'll appreciate how strong those feet muscles actually are. No doubt, you do appreciate how hard those muscles work when you've been on your feet all day and they're starting to cramp and ache. That's when you should consider treating yourself to a foot massage, working your fingers from your heel to the ball of your foot and around your toes. You can make this massage even more effective by using special oils that increase circulation in your feet and help revive tired, weary muscles. Here are a few you can make yourself.

Spicy Cinnamon Foot Oil

This spicy, exotic-smelling oil is wonderful for your feet in two special ways. The two aromatic herbs in it help stimulate circulation, encouraging blood flow throughout your feet to flush out toxins and heal sore muscles. Because cinnamon is antibacterial and cloves are antiseptic, this oil also helps kill germs that cause skin problems of all kinds, including athlete's foot.

Ingredients

    1   cracked cinnamon stick
2–3   cloves
  1/2   cup olive oil

Combine ingredients in small saucepan. Warm on medium heat without boiling. Heat and stir occasionally for ten to fifteen minutes. Remove from heat. Cool completely and then strain to remove fragments. Transfer to glass cork-topped bottle or small plastic squeeze container, such as the kind used for suntan lotions. Apply liberally during massage.

Storage and life span: Store in a cool, dark place. Should keep for about nine months.

TOASTY WARM FOOT RUB

This rub is particularly delightful on cold winter nights when your feet are chilled, tired, and sore. All of the herbs in this batch are ancient medicinals that warm and heal. Sage is a stimulant that increases circulation in your foot muscles. It's also an antiseptic that helps keep your feet germ-free. Rosemary is so invigorating and stimulating to the skin and circulation that some folk doctors used to believe it could actually promote hair growth. And just a few drops of eucalyptus oil can help alleviate muscle strain and fatigue.

Ingredients
- 1/2 cup sunflower oil
- 2 teaspoons dried sage
- 1 teaspoon rosemary
- 1–2 drops eucalyptus essential oil

Combine sunflower oil, sage, and rosemary in small saucepan. Warm on medium heat without boiling. Heat and stir occasionally for ten to fifteen minutes. Remove from heat. Add eucalyptus oil and stir. Cool completely and then strain to remove fragments. Transfer to glass cork-topped bottle or small plastic squeeze container, such as the kind used for suntan lotions. Apply liberally during massage.

Storage and life span: Store in a cool, dark place. Should keep for about nine months.

ROUGH-SKIN-SOFTENING LOTIONS

Since we keep our feet covered much of the time, we don't often get to see the skin on them. In fact, we often downright neglect that skin, which can result in some rather painful, not to mention unsightly, problems such as corns and calluses. Although you can treat foot problems once you have them, the best treatment is to avoid getting them in the first place. One way is to keep the skin on your feet supple and smooth. The following recipes can help you do that.

Avocado Foot Moisturizer

Cut open the tough, leathery skin of the avocado and you'll find rich, buttery green flesh on the inside. This flesh is brimming with essential fatty acids that nourish dry, cracked skin and that offer the perfect way to replace the oils in parched feet. Vitamin E is another important dry-skin ingredient. This vital nutrient is especially important for more mature skin, which tends to be thinner and more easily dried out.

Ingredients
- $1/2$ avocado
- $1/4$ cup olive oil
- 4–5 drops vitamin E oil

Remove pit and spoon out half avocado. Place in blender or food processor along with olive oil and vitamin E oil. Blend on low until ingredients form smooth, uniform, creamy paste.

Pour into small plastic container with lid. Rub liberally on feet, paying special attention to heels, tops of toes, and soles of feet. Work into skin and then rinse well in warm footbath. Pat feet dry.

Storage and life span: Store in the refrigerator. Will last seven to ten days.

SWEET FOOT RELIEF

Next to water, honey may be the oldest beauty product on earth. Ancient Greeks swore by honey to restore youthful vigor to the skin. An outstanding moisturizer and humectant, honey helps the skin retain fluid, leaving it soft and supple. Sugar has natural acids that help remove dead cells to reveal the younger-looking skin underneath. The teaspoon of sugar in this recipe also provides a touch of grittiness, which helps exfoliate tougher patches of rough, dead skin around your heels and the bottoms of your feet.

Ingredients
2 tablespoons honey
1 teaspoon sugar

Combine honey and sugar in small mixing bowl so that sugar grains are evenly distributed throughout honey. Spoon small amounts onto feet and massage gently in circular motions, paying special attention to heels, tops of toes, and soles of feet. Rinse well in warm footbath. Pat feet dry.

Storage and life span: Since the sugar will eventually dissolve completely, this recipe doesn't keep well. It's best to make a new batch before each application.

FOOT POWDERS

You have approximately 250,000 sweat glands in your feet. These glands go into overdrive when you trap your feet in socks or shoes that don't breathe. When these sweat glands create a lot of moisture, bacteria begin to flourish, creating the unpleasant condition we know as foot odor. To beat foot odor, you need to keep your feet dry. One way to do that is to wear socks and shoes that allow your feet to breathe. The other way is to apply a little powder to absorb moisture as you create it. The following recipes not only provide super-absorbent foot protection, they smell fresh and clean, too!

LAVENDER FOOT POWDER

Fragrant and old-fashioned, lavender is one of the best herbs for foot powders. It has a delicate fragrance that leaves your feet smelling clean and pretty, and it's an antiseptic that kills germs that cause foot odors and athlete's foot. The cornstarch in this recipe is highly absorbent, keeping your feet drier longer. And the baking soda makes the powder feel silky-soft on your feet.

Ingredients
- 1/2 cup cornstarch
- 1/3 cup baking soda
- 6–8 drops lavender essential oil

Combine cornstarch and baking soda in medium-sized glass or ceramic mixing bowl. Add couple of drops lavender oil. Sift mixture through sieve or sifter to work oil through powder. Add more oil. Repeat. Keep adding oil and sifting until the oil is completely mixed with powder. Transfer mixture to clean shaker-top container. Powder feet liberally after bathing or showering.

Storage and life span: Store in a cool, dark, and dry place. Should keep up to eight to twelve months.

LEMONY FOOT POWDER

Few natural essences say clean and fresh the way lemon does. We like it so much we put it in furniture cleaners, dishwashing detergents, soap powders, and facial scrubs. You'll also love the lemony-fresh fragrance of this powder. The cornstarch and baking soda provide the moisture-absorbing power you need. And the sesame oil makes the powder especially soft, smooth, and silky. Try it once. You'll never be without it again.

Ingredients
- 3/4 cup cornstarch
- 1/2 cup baking soda
- 4–5 drops lemon essential oil
- 1 teaspoon sesame oil

Combine cornstarch and baking soda in medium-sized glass or ceramic mixing bowl. Add couple of drops of lemon oil. Sift mixture through sieve or sifter to work oil through powder. Add more oil. Repeat. Keep adding oil and sifting until oil is completely mixed with powder. Repeat same steps with sesame oil, adding small amounts and working it through the powder. When oil and powder are well blended, transfer product to clean shaker-top container. Powder your feet liberally after bathing or showering.

Storage and life span: Store in a cool, dark, and dry place. Should keep up to eight to twelve months.

EUCALYPTUS FOOT REFRESHER

Highly aromatic and stimulating, eucalyptus oil makes a perfect natural deodorizer for your feet by killing bacteria and producing a pleasant fragrance. This recipe is made with extra cornstarch to provide maximum moisture-absorbing power. And the handful of baking soda makes the powder soft to the touch.

Ingredients
- 1 cup cornstarch
- 1/4 cup baking soda
- 8–10 drops eucalyptus essential oil

Combine cornstarch and baking soda in medium-sized glass or ceramic mixing bowl. Add couple of drops eucalyptus oil. Sift mixture through sieve or sifter to work oil through powder. Add more oil. Repeat. Keep adding oil and sifting until oil is completely mixed with powder. Transfer to clean shaker-top container. Powder feet liberally after bathing or showering.

Storage and life span: Store in a cool, dark, and dry place. Should keep up to eight to twelve months.

Chapter 10

Easy Beauty Gifts

Once you start making your own personal-care products, you'll find that you want to share them with your friends and family. They'll be sure to appreciate the special care you put into these products. For the next holiday, birthday, wedding, or anniversary, try putting together a special personal-care package for that special someone in your life. Here are a few ideas.

SPECIAL OCCASIONS

CHRISTMAS SPECIAL

The perfect Christmas-season package includes a spicy massage oil, such as Vanilla-Nutmeg Romance, to bring some warmth to cold winter nights; a bottle of Night Magic cologne for those special holiday gatherings; a small tub of Cocoa-Cocoa Lip Protection to keep lips kissably soft; and Nut 'n' Honey Lotion to keep winter skin soft and supple until springtime.

HAPPILY EVER AFTER BASKET

Know someone getting married? Why not send them off on the right foot with a wedding care package? Start out with some sensuous Orange-Cinnamon Revival to rejuvenate the tired couple after dancing their wedding night away. Add a bottle of Just Peachy cologne for her and a bottle of Old-Time Hazel and Sage aftershave for him. If you include some Licorice Lip Gloss to keep their lips soft and moist through all that kissing, some Spicy Cinnamon Foot Oil to relieve their tired feet, and a handful of the fragrant soaps of your choice, you can be sure your favorite newlyweds will have a happy honeymoon. This basket also makes a wonderful anniversary present.

Valentine's Sweetest Gift

Show your love for your sweetie by putting together a package tailor-made for pampering. Include a handful of massage and foot oils such as Toasty Warm Foot Rub, Memories Massage Oil, and Lemony-Ginger Tension Reliever. Add some special pampering products such as Sunny Sunflower Moisturizer and Avocado Foot Moisturizer, and your sweetheart will most certainly be in the mood for love.

Birthday Care Package

Say "Happy Birthday to You" with special personal-care products your loved ones wouldn't necessarily buy for themselves. The silky-soft Lavender Foot Powder is a good start. Add some fresh after-bath splashes and body scrubs such as Rosy Sunshine Scent and Strawberry-Honey Scrub. You could finish off this special care package with some simple soaps and massage oils of your choice.

BOTTLES, BASKETS, AND BOWS

The next time you're at a flea market, garage sale, or second-hand shop, grab a basketful of old-fashioned bottles of all shapes and sizes. These old-time bottles, which typically come in clear, deep blue, light green, and rich red, make perfect containers for personal-care products of all kinds, from rich massage oils to colorful bath crystals. Once you start shopping around, you'll also find ornate bath tins, powder shakers, and even soap dishes and dispensers. Keep your eyes open and you'll find that the possibilities are endless.

While you're shopping around, pick up some wicker and wooden baskets to create pretty care packages and holiday gifts. Nothing says "I love you" more than a basket of pampering care products personally crafted and packaged for the special people in your life.

MAIL-ORDER RESOURCES

Most of the ingredients used in the recipes in this book can be found on the shelves of your local grocery store, health-food store, or pharmacy. If you're having trouble finding some of the essential oils and herbs or want to include an ingredient that is a little more exotic, these mail-order companies can help.

Capitol Drugs, Inc.
4454 Van Nuys Blvd.
Sherman Oaks, California 91403
1-800-858-8833

Gaia Herbs
12 Lancaster County Rd.
Harvard, Massachusetts 01451

Jeanne Rose Aromatherapy
219 Carl St.
San Francisco, California 94117

Origins
767 Fifth Ave.
New York, New York 10153
1-800-ORIGINS

CONVERSIONS
METRIC VOLUME EQUIVALENTS

Measuring Cup

1/4 cup	=	60	mL
1/3 cup	=	75	mL
1/2 cup	=	125	mL
3/4 cup	=	180	mL
1 cup	=	250	mL
2 cups	=	500	mL
3 cups	=	750	mL
4 cups	=	1,000	mL

Tablespoon

1 T	=	15 mL
2 T	=	30 mL
3 T	=	45 mL
4 T	=	60 mL

Teaspoon

1/4 t	=	1 mL
1/2 t	=	2 mL
1 t	=	5 mL
2 t	=	10 mL
3 t	=	15 mL
4 t	=	20 mL

CONVERSIONS
METRIC WEIGHT EQUIVALENTS

1 ounce	=	30 g
4 ounces (1/4 lb.)	=	120 g
12 ounces (3/4 lb.)	=	225 g
16 ounces (1 lb.)	=	360 g
32 ounces (2 lbs.)	=	900 g

OVEN TEMPERATURE EQUIVALENTS

Fahrenheit		Celsius
225°	=	110°
250°	=	120°
275°	=	140°
300°	=	150°
325°	=	160°
350°	=	180°
375°	=	190°
400°	=	200°
425°	=	220°

Notes

Notes